Book H

WORDS TO GO!

WORDS TO KNOW!

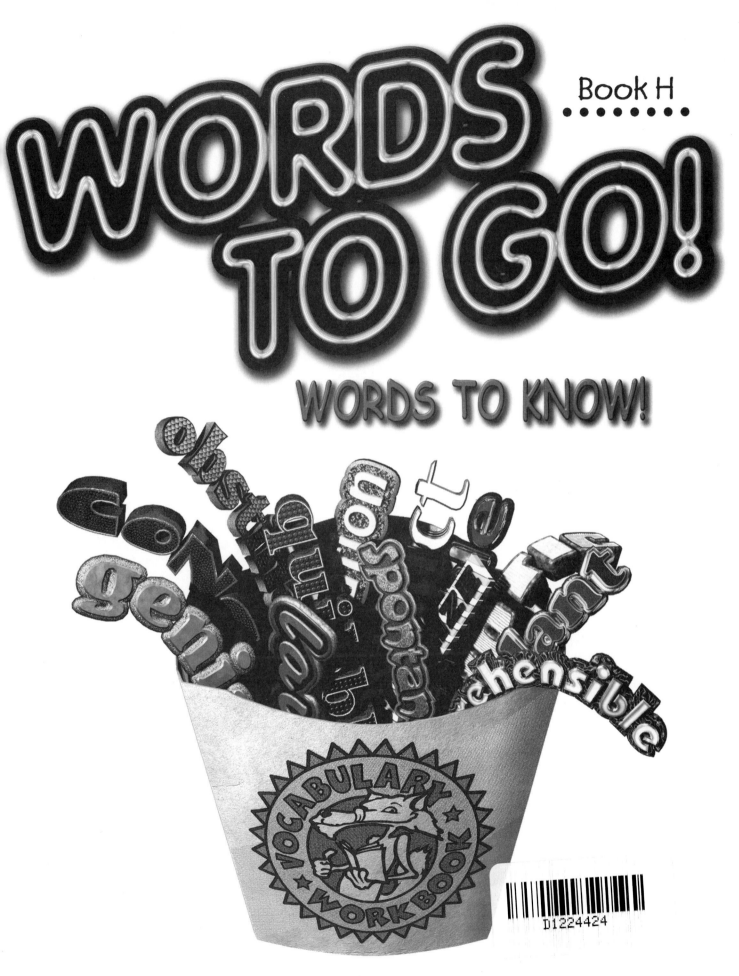

VOCABULARY WORKBOOK

D1224424

Perfection Learning®

Publisher

Perfection Learning® Corporation

Editorial Director   **Julie A. Schumacher**

Editorial Consultant   **Terry Ofner**

Art Director   **Randy Messer**

Concept, Writing, and Design

Sense and Nonsense, Inc.

Writer   **Jan Gleiter**

Designer   **Paul H. Thompson**

5153 North Clark Street, Suite 307
Chicago, Illinois 60640-6823

Tel: 1-773-728-0779

TABLE OF CONTENTS

MADGE: They teach *cow* in Lesson 10! Isn't that sweet?

ISABEL: They told you not to peek ahead.

MADGE: Don't be silly! They can't frighten me or take away my spirit or make me timid!

ISABEL: In other words, they can't cow you.

MADGE: How can they? I'm *already* a cow.

ISABEL: Yes, Madge, a mad cow.

Good morning, class! Did you all have a nice vacation? I hope so, because we have words to learn. We have many words to learn. In fact, I don't know how I can possibly teach so many words! There's only so much time— *(Stop, Molly! Take a breath. Remember what Grandma says! . . . There, I feel better.)* Okay, now, here is how we're going to do it.

• **Neat words.** This book has many words you don't know and some you may know. For all of them, you'll see their most common meanings and sample sentences using them.

• **Easy Pronunciations.** The words are respelled in a way that's easy to understand. I don't know about you, but those symbols that most of the dictionaries use just seem silly.

• **Fun Exercises.** Yes, there are three pages of exercises in each lesson, but they're fun! There are also "Know-How" lessons to give you know-how for what you don't know, um, how.

• **Good Jokes.** They're really funny. Well, except for that one about teachers. And one or two that I didn't quite get. *(Breathe, Molly, breathe!)*

So take out a pen or pencil. Take out some lined paper. Line them up neatly on your desk. Neatness counts, as my grandmother always says.

Now, we've got . . . let's see, 30 lessons with 15 words apiece. So that's, um, 450,000 words. No, no, no, it's 45,000 . . . No, um . . . *(Relax, Molly. Some people just aren't good at multiplication. You're good at . . . being neat. You're nervous, but you're neat.)* Okay, who can tell me how many words are in this book?

A. 30   C. 1,530
B. 450   D. a whole bunch

Actually, that's a trick question because the answer depends on what *words* means. From now on, this book uses **Word** or **Words** when it means the words you're supposed to learn. For example, if it says "write the **Word** that best answers the question," you write the one that best answers the question. Um, got that? Good. Anyway, the answer is 450 **Words**.

Now, to see what's in store for you, read what a few of my former students said. *(It's okay, Molly. It's only your second year of teaching, but there's no way for these eighth-graders to know that.)*

Ulysses S. Granite, *Student, 9th Grade*
My teacher's acquisition of **Words to Go!** and her unswerving devotion to this invaluable program deserve high acclaim. You go, girl!

Frank S. Key, *Student, 9th Grade*
Vocabulary books had always left me apathetic, testy, disgruntled, or just plain bored. So when I first saw **Words to Go,** I winced. I cringed. I ranted. I recoiled. I chafed with indignation. I envisioned yet another heart-rending education fiasco. Now, subsequent to completing the book, I say with contrite humility, boy, was I wrong!

Harriet S. Truman, *Student, 9th Grade*
I liked **WTG** AWB. (That's "a whole bunch.")

Okay, let's all take a deep breath and **get going!**

Miss Molly Morgenstern teaches eighth grade at Salamander School in Okra, Oklahoma.

Know-How

Base Words and Roots

Some words, such as *move*, have only one part. Some, such as *removable*, have several. Every word, short or long, has a main part. This main part is either a "base word" or a "root."

A **base word** is a whole word that can be used to make other words. For example, *agreement, disagreement,* and *agreeable* all contain the base word *agree*. Therefore, each word involves the meaning of *agree*. Not every short word that is seen in a longer one is a base word. For example, in *rebellion*, the base word is *rebel*. Although *bell* and *lion* can be seen, neither one is a base word in *rebellion* because it is not built from either one.

Adding a word part to the end of the base word may slightly change the spelling at the end of the base word. *Happy* is the base word in *happiness*, and *serve* is the base word in *servant*.

Exercise A
Find the base word in each of these words and write it on the line.

1. repayment _____

2. uncomfortable _____

3. precaution _____

4. international _____

5. governmental _____

6. misbehavior _____

7. classification _____

8. enjoyment _____

9. capitalization _____

10. infrequently _____

If the main part of a word is not a whole word, it is called a **root**. For example, the root of *ridicule* is the root *rid*, which means "to laugh." English has roots that come from many different languages, but the two most common ones are Greek and Latin.

This table shows five common roots and their meanings. Use this information to complete Exercise B.

ROOT	MEANING	EXAMPLES
aud	hear	auditorium, audience
cert	sure	certain, certificate
mand	order	command, demand
pend, pens	hang	suspend, pendulum
sens, sent	feel	sensitive, sentimental

Exercise B
Use the table to answer these questions.

____ 11. One animal with *pendulous* ears is
   A. a hawk.   B. a horse.   C. an elephant.

____ 12. A person's *auditory* nerves are found in his or her
   A. nose.   B. ears.   C. backbone.

____ 13. To *ascertain* a fact, you might
   A. repeat it.   B. look it up.   C. write it down.

____ 14. An example of something that is *sentient* is a
   A. rock.   B. daisy.   C. moose.

____ 15. One thing people do because it is *mandatory* is
   A. pay taxes.   B. watch TV.   C. give birthday presents.

Exercise C
Write the base word or the root for each of these words.

16. demand   _____

17. audition   _____

18. unlikeable   _____

19. appendix   _____

20. partial   _____

Exercise D
Read each of these sentences. On the short line, write the base word or the root for the underlined word. On the longer line, write a possible meaning for the underlined word.

21. The soldiers wondered what the general's <u>mandate</u> would be.

   _____   _____

22. Mallory's report of what had happened was <u>credible</u>.

   _____   _____

23. The speech referred to Norman's <u>meritorious</u> actions.

   _____   _____

24. Lily had a <u>combative</u> attitude that surprised us.

   _____   _____

25. Trevor declared with <u>certitude</u> that Lydia was dishonest.

   _____   _____

Know-How

Prefixes

A **prefix** is a word part that is added to the beginning of a base word or a root and that changes its meaning in some way. For example, adding *en-* to *courage* creates *encourage*. Adding *dis-* creates *discourage*. Prefixes are often easy to recognize when they are added to whole words that you know.

Exercise A

Write the prefix contained in each word on the line next to the word.

1. untie _____
2. prepay _____
3. enlarge _____
4. defrost _____
5. semicircle _____

6. impure _____
7. transplant _____
8. enable _____
9. antiwar _____
10. monotone _____

By thinking about how *semi-* changes the meaning of *circle*, you can get a pretty good idea of what *semi-* must mean. You can then use that knowledge when you come across *semi-* at the beginning of other words.

Thinking about what prefixes mean in familiar words such as those above can help you figure out the meanings of unfamiliar words.

Exercise B

Use prefix meanings that you know to figure out what these words mean. Write a meaning for each word.

11. unburden _____
12. preexisting _____
13. enfeeble _____
14. devalue _____
15. semiconscious _____

A prefix that is attached to a root instead of a base word works the same way—it modifies the meaning of the root. Many prefixes, such as *trans-* (which means "across or over"), may be attached to either a base word or a root.

Exercise C

For each word, decide whether *trans-* is attached to a base word or a root. Circle the correct answer.

16. transplant   *base word*   *root*
17. transfer   *base word*   *root*
18. translation   *base word*   *root*
19. transform   *base word*   *root*
20. transmit   *base word*   *root*

Some prefixes have only one meaning, but many prefixes have more than one. For example, *im-* can mean "not" or "in or into."

Exercise D
Circle the meaning that *im-* has in each word.

21.	imprison	*"not"*	*"in or into"*
22.	impure	*"not"*	*"in or into"*
23.	immature	*"not"*	*"in or into"*
24.	immigrate	*"not"*	*"in or into"*
25.	import	*"not"*	*"in or into"*

More often than not, prefixes are attached to roots, not to base words.

Here are a few roots that often have prefixes attached to them.

ROOT	MEANING
pel	to drive
tract	to pull; to drag
ject	to throw

Here are a few common prefixes that are found in many words.

PREFIX	MEANING
dis	apart; away
ex	from; out
pro	forward; ahead; forth
re	back

Exercise E
Form a word for each meaning by attaching one prefix to one root.

26. to throw back _____

27. to drive forward _____

28. to pull out _____

29. to drive away _____

30. to pull back _____

31. to drive out _____

32. to throw forward _____

33. to pull away _____

34. to drive back _____

35. to drag forward _____

Know-How

Suffixes

A **suffix** is a word part that is added to the end of a root or base word and that changes its meaning in some way. The change may be a big one, as when *-less* is added to *hope* or *fear*, but this is rare. Most suffixes just modify a word's meaning, often by changing the tense or part of speech. For example, *laugh* can become *laughed*, *laughter*, or *laughingly*.

A word's spelling may change slightly when a suffix is added. To make *love* into *lovable*, the e is dropped before *-able* is added. The y in *lovely* becomes an i to make *loveliness*. The p in *stop* is doubled to make *stopped* (to keep the short o). Also, some suffixes may or may not include an extra letter. To tame an animal is to *domesticate* it, but to stress a thing is to *accentuate* it (involving an extra u).

Exercise A

Each of these words contains a base word and a suffix. Write the suffix on the line next to each word.

1. national _____

2. productive _____

3. capitalize _____

4. friendship _____

5. mysterious _____

Suffixes are often added to roots instead of to whole words. For example, *purify* contains the base word *pure*. (The e is dropped when *-ify* is added.) But *qualify* adds *-ify* to *qual*, not to a root.

Exercise B

Circle the word in each group that contains a suffix attached to a root instead of to a base word.

6. relaxation   accusation   salvation

7. apologize   utilize   legalize

8. hospital   fictional   personal

9. fertility   activity   dignity

10. fugitive   sensitive   competitive

In order to understand words that have suffixes, you must recognize the suffixes. Even if you don't know exactly what they mean, it helps to realize that they are there. This allows you to look at the base word or the root, which can give you a good clue to a word's meaning. For example, if you know that *-ous* is a common suffix, you can guess that *scandalous* was formed by adding *-ous* to *scandal*.

Exercise C

Find the part of each word that is NOT part of the suffix. Write this word part on the line.

11. customary (minus *-ary*) _____

12. magnitude (minus *-tude*) _____

13. terrorize (minus *-ize*) _____

14. mystify (minus *-ify*) _____

15. minimize (minus *-ize*) _____

This table shows common suffixes and their meanings. Use this information to complete the rest of the exercises.

SUFFIX	MEANING	EXAMPLES
ary	relating to or connected with	imaginary, complimentary
ate	to cause to be	activate, decorate
ee	receiver of action or one who is	absentee, employee
istic	relating to	realistic, artistic
ition	act, condition, or result of	addition, competition

Exercise D
Write the letter of the word that matches each clue.

A. simplistic
B. cautionary
C. supposition
D. addressee
E. differentiate

____ 16. This is the person who is supposed to receive a letter or package.

____ 17. This describes an approach that fails to see how complex a problem is.

____ 18. This describes a comment or story that contains a warning.

____ 19. This is what you do when you distinguish between things.

____ 20. This is something you don't know for sure but you think is true.

Exercise E
Use what you know about suffixes and base words or roots to complete each statement.

____ 21. A *momentary* pause is one that is
A. brief. B. necessary. C. unexpected.

____ 22. An *examinee* is someone who
A. needs help. B. tells a story. C. takes a test.

____ 23. An *individualistic* response is one that is
A. wise. B. personal. C. required.

____ 24. To *liberate* an animal would be to
A. free it. B. train it. C. protect it.

____ 25. When you act on your own *volition*, you act
A. by choice. B. foolishly. C. in a sneaky way.

Know-How

Homographs

Some words, called **homographs**, have the same spelling although they have different meanings. (The word *homograph* comes from roots meaning "same" and "to write."). When both or all of the meanings of these words are familiar to you, they usually don't cause confusion.

Exercise A
Circle the letter of the correct meaning for each underlined word.

1. Can fighters with spears defeat ones with superior <u>arms</u>?
   A. weapons
   B. limbs on the upper body

2. Before going out, please put on a <u>fresh</u> shirt.
   A. rude, sassy, or too bold
   B. not worn or soiled; clean

3. Dolores has a small <u>mole</u> on one side of her forehead.
   A. a dark spot on the skin
   B. a small, burrowing mammal

4. <u>Pupils</u> get larger in dim light and smaller in bright light.
   A. dark openings in the center of the eyes
   B. people learning from a teacher or expert

Sometimes a word that looks familiar doesn't make sense in a particular sentence. For example, "I got ready to *tender* my apology." Clearly, *tender* does not mean either "easily chewed" or "softly affectionate." It isn't even used as an adjective. It must have another meaning, and indeed it does. *Tender* can mean "to offer or present for acceptance."

Exercise B
Each underlined word has several meanings. Write the word in each sentence that someone would most likely need to look up in a dictionary.

5. All <u>period</u>, we discussed the <u>content</u> of the chapter, so now I know about the British practice of <u>impressing</u> American sailors.

   _____

6. A <u>row</u> of <u>fans</u> waited to <u>fawn</u> over the movie star.

   _____

7. Did the <u>rock</u> just <u>graze</u> you, or did you get knocked <u>down</u>?

   _____

8. It was a <u>lie</u> and a <u>base</u> attempt to <u>hide</u> the truth.

   _____

Although a dictionary will provide the meanings for homographs, you still have to decide which word and which meaning is the one you need to know. Look at these sample dictionary entries for what the word *mean* can mean.

---

mean¹ *verb* **1.** to intend; to have in mind *[I mean to leave immediately.]* **2.** to express; to stand for or indicate *[What did you mean by giving me that look?]* **3.** to say truly; to speak or act sincerely *[When you hugged her, did you mean it?]* **4.** to have a certain amount of importance *[My family means a great deal to me.]*

mean² *adjective* **1.** unkind *[Don't be mean to your little brother.]* **2.** stingy *[to be mean with one's money]* **3.** skillful; expert *[She can play a mean game of tennis.]*

Exercise C

Write the letter that matches the meaning that the word *mean* has in each sentence.

A. **mean**¹, definition 1
B. **mean**¹, definition 2
C. **mean**¹, definition 3
D. **mean**¹, definition 4
E. **mean**², definition 1
F. **mean**², definition 2
G. **mean**², definition 3

_____ 9. How much does freedom *mean* to you?

_____ 10. Don't be *mean* in how much of a donation you give.

_____ 11. Rocco *means* to be a doctor someday.

_____ 12. Deborah's *mean* remark hurt Sheila's feelings.

_____ 13. That gesture from the umpire *means* the runner is out.

_____ 14. Are you kidding, or do you *mean* it?

_____ 15. Their best player has a *mean* jump shot from the three-point line.

Know-How

Using What
You Know

When you come across an unfamiliar word, there are several ways to find out its meaning. Two of the best are to ask someone who knows or look it up in a dictionary. Those methods are not always available, but something else is—your own knowledge. You can often get at least a good idea of a word's meaning by using what you already know.

If you had to learn every single word one at a time, it would take forever. Luckily, most words have connections to other words. You can use those connections.

Example: *disallow = dis + allow*
allow means "permit"
disagree means "not agree"
disallow means "not allow"

So, if a judge *disallows* some piece of evidence during a trial, the judge refuses to allow it to be used. Sometimes, even if parts of a word are familiar, you won't be able to figure out exactly what the word means. However, you may be able to get a good idea about its meaning. Look at it carefully to see if you recognize any parts of it.

Example: *circumspect = circum + spect*
circum is found in *circumference*—the distance around a circle
spect is . . . a root. It's in *inspect*, *spectacles*, and *spectator*, and it has to do with seeing or looking.
circumspect . . . "around looking?" That doesn't make sense. How about "looking around"?

If you read the sentence, "A banker must be *circumspect*," the idea of "looking around" would make some sense. A banker—or anyone else—who is looking around is cautious and careful, and that's exactly what *circumspect* means.

Exercise A
For each "hard" word, write the base word. Think about it and about a familiar word. Then use what you know to answer each question.

1. dethrone _____

   Think about *defrost*. What might *dethrone* mean?

   _____

2. interstate _____

   Think about *international*. What might *interstate* mean?

   _____

3. unmask _____

   Think about *untie*. What might *unmask* mean?

   _____

Unfamiliar words aren't always long, and they can't always be broken up into familiar parts. Still, you can often get a lot of help by thinking about words that you already know.

Exercise B

Use what you know about the underlined word to figure out what the word in italics means. Write the letter of the answer on the line.

_____ 4. By thinking about <u>combat</u>, you can tell that a *combatant* is someone who is
A. running.   B. fighting.   C. pretending.

_____ 5. By thinking about <u>ammunition</u>, you can tell that *munitions* could include
A. rifles.   B. shovels.   C. pots and pans.

_____ 6. By thinking about <u>error</u>, you can tell that to *err* is to make
A. a list.   B. a mistake.   C. an effort.

_____ 7. By thinking about <u>impossible</u> and <u>penetrate</u>, you can tell that something that is *impenetrable* cannot be
A. seen.   B. imagined.   C. cut through.

_____ 8. By thinking about <u>desire</u>, you can tell that someone who is *desirous* of food feels
A. full.   B. hungry.   C. disgusted.

_____ 9. By thinking about <u>saliva</u>, you can tell that if something makes you *salivate*, your
A. eyes sting.   B. head hurts.   C. mouth waters.

_____ 10. By thinking about <u>endure</u>, you can tell that something that has *durability* will
A. last.   B. break.   C. disappear.

_____ 11. By thinking about <u>penalty</u>, you can tell that a *penal* institution is a
A. prison.   B. hospital.   C. university.

_____ 12. By thinking about <u>nonsense</u> and <u>existence</u>, you can tell that a thing that is *nonexistent* is
A. huge.   B. brand new.   C. only imaginary.

Know-How

Context Clues

Except in something like a spelling list, a word almost always appears in a paragraph, sentence, or phrase. These other words that are used with the word are its **context**. The context of a word always supplies some sort of clue to its meaning. At the very least, a reader can tell what part of speech the word is by the way it's used. And sometimes a great deal more information is provided.

For example:

Was that a *prevarication*?
Prevarication is a noun.

I will be upset if I hear a *prevarication* from him.
A *prevarication* is something that probably isn't good.

His remark was designed to hide the truth, and this *prevarication* angered me.
Prevarication is a noun that means "a statement made to hide the truth."

The last example for *prevarication* actually provides a definition of the word. Context clues do not often provide this much help, but they do occasionally.

A common kind of context clue is one that provides a word that means the same, or almost the same, thing.

For example:

Time will *efface* the sign as wind and rain slowly erase the words.
This suggests that *efface* and *erase* are similar in meaning.

Ramsey's *exertion* left him gasping, for he was not used to making such a considerable effort.
This makes it clear that an exertion is a considerable effort.

Another useful kind of context clue tells you that something is the opposite of something else, or at least quite different.

For example:

Michelle tried to *dissuade* me, but everyone else encouraged me.
To dissuade someone is very different from encouraging someone.

Matsuo doesn't *loathe* cats; on the contrary, he loves them!
Loathe and *love* must have opposite meanings.

Another way that context clues can help is by giving one or more examples.

For example:

The way they lied, cheated, stole, and bullied smaller children made me wonder if they had any *ethics* at all.
Lying, cheating, stealing, and bullying are all bad things to do, so ethics are probably similar to morals.

The *maladies* included measles and chicken pox in the children; arthritis and heart problems in the elderly; and colds and flu in all groups.
The things mentioned are illnesses, so a malady is almost certainly an illness.

Although context clues rarely tell you exactly what a word means, they do often give you an idea about its meaning.

Exercise

Use context clues to get an idea of what the underlined word means. Write the letter of the word's likely meaning on the line.

_____ 1. Nowadays, dentists are able to <u>desensitize</u> the area of your mouth they need to work on, so drilling and filling teeth doesn't hurt.
   A. numb
   B. examine
   C. identify
   D. thoroughly clean

_____ 2. Most club members went along with the plan, but Claire <u>dissented</u>.
   A. voted
   B. joined
   C. disagreed
   D. left quickly

_____ 3. Please <u>apprise</u> Ms. Welch as soon as possible; Mr. Okada also wants to be notified.
   A. hire
   B. inform
   C. relieve
   D. interview

_____ 4. Noah took the paper in a <u>surreptitious</u> way so that no one else would notice.
   A. selfish
   B. sneaky
   C. dramatic
   D. annoying

_____ 5. Gardening, painting watercolors, making birdhouses, and collecting stamps were Casey's <u>avocations</u>.
   A. fears
   B. goals
   C. chores
   D. hobbies

_____ 6. Reese was <u>indigent</u> as a young man, but his cleverness and hard work eventually made him wealthy.
   A. poor
   B. stubborn
   C. foolish
   D. spoiled

_____ 7. He was most interested in the <u>fauna</u> of the region; its bears, deer, birds, rabbits, and raccoons all fascinated him.
   A. climate
   B. customs
   C. history
   D. animals

_____ 8. The two nations had been <u>adversaries</u> for more than a hundred years—working against each other's goals and, from time to time, exploding into war.
   A. friends
   B. neighbors
   C. enemies
   D. democracies

Know-How

Analogies 1

An **analogy** is a way of comparing things that have similar relationships.

Example: A baby <u>deer</u> is called a <u>fawn</u>, just as a baby <u>sheep</u> is called a <u>lamb</u>.

Exercise A
Fill in the blank with a word that completes each analogy.

1. A <u>maple</u> is a type of <u>tree</u>,
   just as a <u>tulip</u> is a type of   _____

2. A <u>cup</u> is half of a <u>pint</u>,
   just as a <u>nickel</u> is half of a   _____

3. <u>Dry</u> is the opposite of <u>wet</u>,
   just as <u>short</u> is the opposite of   _____

4. <u>Hamburger</u> comes from a <u>cow</u>,
   just as <u>bacon</u> comes from a   _____

5. <u>Gold</u> is a precious <u>metal</u>;
   just as a <u>diamond</u> is a precious   _____

The above analogies tell what the relationship is. The analogies you will see on worksheets and tests usually do not provide this information. Instead, they usually look like this:

bird : flock :: horse : ?

To complete an analogy like this, you have to figure out how the first two words go together. Make up a sentence that describes the relationship. "A group of <u>birds</u> is called a <u>flock</u>." (Sometimes you will need to add an *s* to a word, as with *birds*.) Then think about how to finish the analogy. Use the same "explanation" words. "A group of <u>horses</u> is called a <u>herd</u>."

Examples: *car : garage*   A shelter for a <u>car</u> is a <u>garage</u>.
              chapter : book   A <u>chapter</u> is part of a <u>book</u>.
              angry : furious   Someone extremely <u>angry</u> is <u>furious</u>.
              stapler : fasten   A <u>stapler</u> is used to <u>fasten</u> things

Exercise B
Write a short sentence that describes the relationship between each pair of words. This exercise continues on the next page.

6. *attic : top*   _____

                      _____

7. *old : young*   _____

                      _____

8. *boat : water*   _____

                      _____

9. *robin : worm* _____

_____

10. *shoe : foot* _____

_____

Analogies involve two relationships, not just one, and those two relationships must be the same. So, after you figure out the relationship between the first two words, you must find another pair of words that go together the same way. You can do this by putting the new words in the sentence you made up and seeing which ones make sense.

Example: *violin : orchestra :: shirt :*
  A. cloth   C. pants
  B. button   D. wardrobe

Step 1: A <u>violin</u> is part of an <u>orchestra</u>.

Step 2: A. A <u>shirt</u> is part of a <u>cloth</u>.
  B. A <u>shirt</u> is part of a <u>button</u>.
  C. A <u>shirt</u> is part of a <u>pants</u>.
  D. A <u>shirt</u> is part of a <u>wardrobe</u>.

Step 3: Answer D is the only one that makes a sensible sentence.

Exercise C
Choose the word that completes each analogy. Write the letter on the line.

____ 11. *painter : brush :: carpenter :*
  A. house   C. wall
  B. hammer   D. worker

____ 12. *tiptoe : walk :: whisper :*
  A. talk   C. giggle
  B. sneak   D. scream

____ 13. *lettuce : head :: bread :*
  A. flour   C. loaf
  B. butter   D. bakery

____ 14. *hide : reveal :: scold :*
  A. frown   C. like
  B. criticize   D. praise

____ 15. *beagle : dog :: canary :*
  A. bird   C. cage
  B. song   D. feathers

Know-How

Analogies 2

There are many kinds of relationships that are used in analogies. Here are some common kinds.

		Examples
A.	Synonyms	*help : assist :: desire : want*
B.	Antonyms	*straight : crooked :: bumpy : smooth*
C.	Part to Whole	*verse : song :: course : meal*
D.	Place	*oven : kitchen :: dresser : bedroom*
E.	Characteristic	*parrot : beak :: elephant : trunk*
F.	Object and Purpose	*hammer : pound :: saw : cut*
G.	Example	*canoe : boat :: biography : book*
H.	Manner	*shuffle : walk :: mumble : talk*
I.	Degree or Intensity	*bad : terrible :: old : ancient*
J.	Grammatical	*run : ran :: see : saw*

Exercise A

Decide which type of relationship each word pair involves. On the line, write the letter from the list above.

____ 1. *soap : wash*

____ 2. *finger : hand*

____ 3. *add : subtract*

____ 4. *she : her*

____ 5. *unhappy : miserable*

____ 6. *peek : look*

____ 7. *love : emotion*

____ 8. *rabbit : fur*

Sometimes the first two words in an analogy can go together in several ways. You may have to guess about the right way to explain their relationship. You know your guess is right if only one answer choice works. What should you do if more than one answer works?

Example: run : jog :: walk :
          A. hop   C. stroll
          B. march   D. hurry

Sentence: <u>Run</u> and <u>jog</u> have similar meanings.

Result: Two answers are correct:
        <u>Walk</u> and <u>march</u> have similar meanings.
        <u>Walk</u> and <u>stroll</u> have similar meanings.

Only one answer can be the correct one, so you have to come up with a sentence that explains the relationship between the first two words more exactly.

Sentence: To <u>run</u> in a slow manner is to <u>jog</u>.

Result: Now, only one answer is correct:
        To <u>walk</u> in a slow manner is to <u>stroll</u>.

Exercise B

Choose the word that completes each analogy. Write the letter on the line.

____ 9. *stem : flower :: trunk :*
    A. bark   C. tree
    B. forest   D. roots

____ 10. *mansion : house :: ship :*
    A. boat   C. sailor
    B. ocean   D. voyage

____ 11. *ice : cold :: rock :*
    A. hard   C. small
    B. smooth   D. sharp

____ 12. *ask : reply :: hold :*
    A. grab   C. take
    B. divide   D. release

Some analogies require you to choose the whole second pair. You should work this kind the same way, by figuring out how the first pair goes together.

Example: *squirrel : nut ::*
                A. bee : hive   C. tree : leaf
                B. rabbit : carrot   D. sheep : wool

Answer: A logical sentence that describes the first pair is "A squirrel likes to eat nuts." The only pair that has the same relationship is B.

Exercise C

Decide which pair of words completes each analogy. Write the letter on the line.

____ 13. *harm : destruction ::*
    A. regret : apology   C. pleasure : enjoyment
    B. kindness : cruelty   D. goodness : perfection

____ 14. *car : wheel ::*
    A. boat : water   C. train : caboose
    B. sled : runner   D. bike : handlebar

____ 15. *trout : fish ::*
    A. lion : tiger   C. wasp : insect
    B. uncle : nephew   D. teacher : student

Lesson 1

alternative *all•TUR•nuh•tiv*

NOUN something that is one of two possible choices [I don't feel like studying, but the *alternative* is doing poorly on tomorrow's test.]

ADJECTIVE offering another possibility [Is there an *alternative* activity for those who don't like fishing?]

appease *uh•PEEZ* VERB

to make more peaceful and less angry, hateful, or upset [Betsy tried to *appease* the neighbors by offering to pay for the window she broke.]

disperse *di•SPURCE* VERB

1. to break up and scatter [The police tried to *disperse* the crowd that had gathered.]

2. to spread around; to distribute [The United Way *disperses* funds to a variety of charities.]

exempt *eg•ZEMPT*

VERB to release (someone) from something that applies to others [Miss Ito will *exempt* anyone with an *A* average from the final test.]

ADJECTIVE free from some requirement that applies to others [Arletta seems to think that she's *exempt* from the rules.]

induce *in•DOOCE* VERB

to lead (someone or something) to act in a certain way or to do something; to cause [A store may *induce* people to make purchases by putting items on sale.]

lackluster *LAK•luss•tur* ADJECTIVE

without brightness, liveliness, or excellence; lacking energy [Due to a bad headache, Gretchen gave a *lackluster* performance.]

nocturnal *nok•TUR•nul* ADJECTIVE

1. done or happening during the night [The cat's *nocturnal* search for mice kept me awake.]

2. active at night [Owls are *nocturnal* birds that sleep all day and hunt during the night.]

opportune *op•ur•TOON* ADJECTIVE

particularly convenient or suitable in time; coming at just the right time [When Dad mentioned his raise, it seemed an *opportune* moment to tell him I needed money for a field trip.]

pedestal *PED•us•tul* NOUN

a stand on which something is or could be placed [Each column was supported by a marble *pedestal*.]

receptive *ri•SEP•tiv* ADJECTIVE

ready or willing to receive; inclined to take a suggestion or consider a possibility [Nicole seems *receptive* to our plan, so I think we can count on her.]

spindly *SPIND•lee* ADJECTIVE

long and thin in a way that suggests a lack of strength [The legs of the chair looked too *spindly* to hold anyone's weight.]

status *STAT•us* or *STATE•us* NOUN

1. one's position in relation to others [Gene is very popular, and his *status* in the school will make him hard to beat in the election.]

2. the condition or state of something at a particular time [What is the *status* of your history report; are you almost finished with it?]

stipulation *stip•yoo•LAY•shun*

NOUN a demand or condition of an agreement [I can use the car with the *stipulation* that I fill the gas tank.]

traumatic *traw•MAT•ik* ADJECTIVE

seriously harmful, either emotionally or physically; having a lasting bad effect [Being accidentally locked in a closet was so *traumatic* that Katie still can't stand to be in a small space.]

unparalleled *un•PAIR•uh•leld*

ADJECTIVE having no equal; unmatched [We saw many lovely places, but the beauty of the Grand Canyon was *unparalleled*.]

ASK THE ZOOKEEPER

Dear Z:
What nocturnal animals are the funniest?
Brady

Dear B:
I can't say for sure, but I do know the owls are a real hoot!

Exercise A: Mini-Rhyme Time

Write the **Word** that best completes each rhyme.

USE A **WORD** ONLY ONE
TIME IN EACH EXERCISE.

1. If a large fowl won't release your finger from its beak, you have to figure out a way to ___ the goose to let loose.

    _____

2. A requirement that every country take part in something is a ___ for the participation of each nation.

    _____

3. If an army officer wrote in a diary every evening, what he wrote might be called the colonel's ___ journal entries.

    _____

4. If you intend to send one of two poems to hundreds of people but, by mistake, send the one that isn't as good, you ___ the worse verse.

    _____

Dear Keeper:
My rabbit won't come out of my hat! As you might imagine, this results in a very lackluster trick. Got any ideas?
  Gert the Great

Dear Great:
It's having a bad hare day. (By the way, I used to do that trick too, but my hat's gone missing.)

Exercise B: When . . .

Write the **Word** that best completes each sentence.

5. When there's a second road you can take to avoid traffic, that road is a handy . . . .

    _____

6. When a person is positively the best at doing something, his or her skill is . . . .

    _____

7. When new supplies arrive right before existing supplies run out, their arrival is . . . .

    _____

8. When a person is hurt so badly that he or she may not recover, the injury is . . . .

    _____

9. When you listen to what other people say and let their ideas affect you, you are . . . .

    _____

10. When a statue is displayed in a museum but not put on the floor, it often sits on a . . . . .

    _____

11. When a person hears rustling in the woods at night, animals making those noises are . . . .

    _____

12. When you ask how far along the party preparations are, you want to know their . . . . . .

    _____

Exercise C: Synonyms

Write the **Word** that could be used in place of each underlined word or phrase. This exercise continues on the next page.

13. Athletes who tend to be <u>accepting of and open</u> to coaching are likely to improve.

    _____

14. A note from your doctor is needed to <u>excuse</u> you from gym class.

    _____

15. Sylvia's social <u>level</u> is very important to her.

_____

16. Is there any <u>other</u> method of accomplishing this?

_____

17. My grandmother's brownies are <u>superior to any others</u>.

_____

18. A heron's legs look too <u>frail</u> to support such a large bird.

_____

19. The student council will <u>hand out</u> funds from the bake sale.

_____

20. Syrup of Ipecac is a medicine that will <u>bring on</u> vomiting.

_____

21. The birdbath has a bowl section and a two-foot-tall <u>base</u>.

_____

22. Our accidental meeting turned out to be <u>timely</u>.

_____

Exercise D: True or False
Circle TRUE or FALSE for each statement.

23. Rude remarks from a clerk are likely to **appease** an irritated shopper.	TRUE	FALSE
24. Driving in a car is an **alternative** to flying from Boston to Chicago.	TRUE	FALSE
25. Sudden rain as a picnic begins would be considered **opportune**.	TRUE	FALSE
26. Rewards may be used to **induce** people to do something.	TRUE	FALSE
27. Being in a bad car accident would be a **traumatic** event. . . .	TRUE	FALSE
28. **Lackluster** efforts usually earn a worker high praise. . . .	TRUE	FALSE
29. A detailed contract contains **stipulations**.	TRUE	FALSE

Exercise E: Antonyms
Write the Word that means the opposite of each underlined word or phrase.

Dear Señor:
Why does a giraffe have such a long neck? *Manuel*

Dear Amigo:
A giraffe's body is so far away from its head that there's no alternative.

30. Weightlifting can turn ___ arms into <u>sturdy and strong</u> ones.

_____

31. I tried to ___ Mrs. Foster, but my remarks just seemed to <u>anger</u> her more.

_____

32. If loud noises ___ a flock of sheep, the herder must <u>gather</u> them again.

_____

33. A ___ mind can consider new ideas, but a <u>closed</u> one just rejects them.

_____

34. I'll need to work on this ___ speech a great deal if I want it to be <u>brilliant</u>.

_____

35. Charities are ___ from taxes, but businesses are <u>responsible</u> for paying them.

_____

Quick LIST

alternative N., ADJ.	exempt V., ADJ.	opportune ADJ.	status N.
appease V.	induce V.	pedestal N.	stipulation N.
disperse V.	lackluster ADJ.	receptive ADJ.	traumatic ADJ.
	nocturnal ADJ.	spindly ADJ.	unparalleled ADJ.

Exercise F: Fill-in

Write the Word that best completes each sentence.

36. Don't try to give Edmund advice; he won't be _____ to it at all.

37. This new shampoo claims it can add shine to _____ hair; I hope it works.

38. Babe Ruth's record number of home runs was _____ for many years.

39. It is a bad idea to hang the tire swing from a _____ tree branch; it may break.

40. I can go out tonight, but my parents made the _____ that I be home by 10:00.

41. Extremely loud banging at our front door by a _____ visitor awakened us at one in the morning.

42. A two-for-one discount was good enough to _____ us to try the new restaurant.

43. Dylan thinks that a car indicates its owner's _____ and that people will look up to him if he drives a fancy one.

44. Humphrey tried to think of some _____ plan in case his first one didn't work.

45. I accidentally kicked a _____ that a plant was sitting on, and the plant crashed to the floor.

46. Some men were _____ from the military during World War II because of poor health or other reasons.

47. A dog that has _____ experiences as a puppy may grow up to be fearful its whole life.

48. It was quite _____ for the police car to drive by just as the robber fled the convenience store.

49. Parents who try to _____ a child who has frequent temper tantrums may end up with a spoiled child.

50. It took the guests a long time to _____ after the party because no one wanted to leave.

Dear Zook:
Once I saw you in the elephant pen, hopping around like the ground was on fire. What was that?
Hester

Dear Hest:
If a pen hasn't been cleaned after animals have . . . Well, um, walking in certain areas can be a little traumatic.

"Gotta go try to appease the great apes. Hat trick used to do it. Guess I'll try the old saw-the-gorilla-in-half trick instead. Wish me luck!"

Lesson 2 _____

astute *uh•STOOT* ADJECTIVE

clever and sharp-minded; showing a thorough and deep understanding [Uncle Kenny is an *astute* lawyer; there isn't much about legal matters that he doesn't know.]

bias *BY•us*

NOUN a strong leaning for or against something that is based on personal preference or a set idea [The store owner seemed to have a *bias* against teenagers and refused to hire me.]

VERB to cause to look favorably or unfavorably on; to create a bias [Shelly looked as sweet as she could in an effort to *bias* the jury.]

compile *kum•PILE* VERB

1. to gather together and put in order [After Mrs. Lee *compiles* the receipts, we'll know exactly how much we've spent.]

2. to create something by collecting materials from a variety of sources [The chef will *compile* the best recipes into one cookbook.]

destitute *DESS•ti•toot* ADJECTIVE

extremely poor; without basic necessities [The *destitute* people in the refugee camp had little food and almost no medicine.]

enhance *en•HANCE* VERB

to make greater or heighten; to add to in a way that improves [Putting in a swimming pool would *enhance* the value of the property.]

extraneous *ex•TRAY•nee•us* ADJECTIVE

not needed or not related to what is being considered or dealt with [Since only soup was served, the forks on the table were *extraneous*.]

fabricate *FAB•ri•kate* VERB

1. to make or manufacture [This factory *fabricates* various kinds of machine parts.]

2. to make up; to create something untrue [The girl hoped she could *fabricate* a story that would keep her from being punished.]

flaunt *FLAWNT* VERB

to show off [The man took every opportunity to *flaunt* his build by flexing his muscles.]

heyday *HEY•day* NOUN

the time of greatest success or strength [In their *heyday*, that band was at the top of the charts week after week.]

illegible *ih•LEJ•uh•bul* ADJECTIVE

impossible to read due to sloppy or faint writing or printing [The sign was so weather-beaten that it had become *illegible*.]

intuition *in•too•ISH•un* NOUN

an understanding or knowledge of something without the use of reasoning [Peter's *intuition* told him that Gwen was a person he could trust completely.]

lush *LUSH* ADJECTIVE

1. growing thickly or heavily [The rain forest is full of *lush* vegetation and amazing creatures.]

2. luxurious [Having grown up in much more *lush* surroundings, the princess had difficulty in adjusting to a cottage in the woods.]

Question:
What happened to the salad recipe as the chef compiled his cookbook?

renown *ri•NOWN* NOUN

fame; good reputation [The scientist gained *renown* for her successful work in chemistry and eventually won the Nobel Prize.]

sedate *si•DATE*

ADJECTIVE calm, serious, and proper [At first, the party guests were *sedate*, but they loosened up when the dancing started.]

VERB to calm with medication [It is often helpful to *sedate* a patient before setting a broken bone.]

vigil *VIJ•ul* NOUN

a period of watch, usually during a time when one would normally be asleep; the act of staying awake to watch over [The sick child's parents took turns keeping a *vigil* over her.]

Words to Go!

Exercise A: Mini-Rhyme Time
Write the Word that best completes each rhyme.

USE A WORD ONLY ONE
TIME IN EACH EXERCISE.

1. A woman with a mild, polite, solemn husband has a ___ mate.

_____

2. A senator whose hunches are good is a politician with ___.

_____

3. A village well known for its charm is a town with ___.

_____

4. When you put forms inside a folder, you ___ a file.

_____

5. I put bright patches on my jeans to ___ my pants.

_____

6. Someone who knows everything about pears, oranges, and bananas is ___ about fruit.

_____

7. When plants grow thickly beneath the trees, the woods have ___ underbrush.

_____

Answer: He tossed it. (printed upside down)

Exercise B: What Is It?
Write the Word that each clue describes.

"It seemed extraneous. Especially the parsley."

8. A tailor might use a sewing machine, wool, and a pattern to do this to a suit.

_____

9. To print a book of stories by different authors, a publisher must first do this to the stories.

_____

10. If you scribble over a word, this describes that word.

_____

11. Sticking to the point means leaving out this kind of detail.

_____

12. If your feelings are strong, they may do this to your judgment.

_____

13. People seek this when they try to "make a name" for themselves.

_____

Exercise C: Synonyms
Write the Word that could be used in place of each underlined word or phrase. This exercise continues on the next page.

14. When my dad was a boy, his family was <u>penniless</u>.

_____

15. Margaret liked to <u>make a show of</u> her new diamond ring by waving her hand about.

_____

16. During the <u>peak</u> of her stardom, Monica Montana was making several movies each year.

_____

17. Several firefighters kept a <u>lookout</u> throughout the day in case the fire started up again.

_____

18. Ada made <u>intelligent and sensitive</u> comments about the poem.
    _____

19. Aunt Corinne, who is usually quite <u>dignified and quiet</u>, surprised me by shrieking.
    _____

20. You can fit things into a small suitcase if you leave out items that are <u>not essential</u>.
    _____

Exercise D: Antonyms

Write the **Word** that means the opposite of each underlined word or phrase.

21. During this <u>low period</u> in her career, Mrs. Martinez thought back to when she was in her ___.
    _____

22. Brendan's remarks weren't <u>ignorant</u>; they were quite ___.
    _____

23. Umpires must show <u>open-minded fairness</u>, not any kind of ___.
    _____

24. Will costumes <u>take away</u> from our presentation or ___ it?
    _____

25. Copy that over so that the words are <u>neat and clear</u> instead of ___.
    _____

26. If fear and pain <u>stir up</u> patients, they may need a drug to ___ them.
    _____

27. Dolly used <u>logic</u> to solve the problem, but Molly used ___.
    _____

28. Some rich people <u>conceal</u> their wealth while others ___ it.
    _____

29. I chose a <u>plain, simple</u> motel since I couldn't afford a ___ resort.
    _____

30. Though my family isn't <u>well-to-do</u>, we're not ___ either.
    _____

Exercise E: Other Forms of Words

Use what you know about the **Words** to choose the correct answers.

_____ 31. In order to be **vigilant**, a person must be
    A. wise.   B. alert.   C. brave.

_____ 32. If you say "That's a total **fabrication**," you mean that it's a
    A. lie.   B. joke.   C. secret.

_____ 33. A group of people who often live in **destitution** are
    A. tourists.   B. movie stars.   C. the homeless.

_____ 34. You might describe an **intuitive** response as being a
    A. "team effort."   B. "gut feeling."   C. "slip of the tongue."

_____ 35. Something that people often use as an **enhancement** to their appearance is
    A. make-up.   B. a disguise.   C. a mirror.

There was a cowboy whose heyday had long since come and gone. One day he was thrown from his horse. "Someone help!" he called out. "I've fallen, and I can't giddyup!" ∎

Exercise F: Fill-in

Write the **Word** that best completes each sentence.

36. Those _____ vines cover the window and keep my room dim and cool.

37. Mom's _____ always seems to kick in when I'm not telling the truth.

38. During its _____, the Roman Empire was spread across three continents.

39. An actor's _____ will increase after he or she wins an Oscar.

40. Raul tends to _____ his ability to speak French, and it's getting pretty annoying.

41. Anabela is so _____; no one ever has to tell her to settle down.

42. My cousin can _____ an excuse, on the spot, for almost anything he doesn't want to do.

43. Grandma has a _____ against younger doctors; she won't see one who's under forty.

44. Researchers may _____ data from several studies and experiments to prove an idea.

45. The quarterback's _____ play-calling resulted in several quick scores.

46. Some children are so _____ that they don't own a single pair of shoes.

47. The loyal collie kept a _____ at the injured boy's side until help arrived.

48. Scary music was used to _____ the suspense in the movie.

49. The name on this paper is _____; I have no idea who it belongs to.

50. Mom says Dad's hairbrushes are _____ now that he's totally bald.

Exercise G: Writing

On your own paper, write a very brief story using any FIVE of the **Words** in any order. The joke on the right does this, but your story doesn't need to be funny. Make it about any subject you like. Just don't make it *illegible*.

Milly compiled a list of demands. When intuition told her the time was right, she went to see her boss. "I'm your best employee, but to keep me, you'll have to give me a $20,000 raise and enhance my benefits."

Being an astute businesswoman, the boss said sedately, "What would you think of a $100,000 raise, eight weeks of vacation each year, plus a lush new company car?"

Milly gasped. "Are you kidding me?"

"Yup," the boss said, "but you started it." ■

Lesson 3

amass *uh•MASS* VERB

to gather together a large amount [Over the years, my aunt has managed to *amass* a huge collection of rare books.]

apt *APT* ADJECTIVE

1. exactly right for some purpose [Virginia used an *apt* quotation to make her point.]

2. quick to learn or understand [Carlo is quite an *apt* piano student.]

3. likely [You are *apt* to fall if you run on that slippery surface.]

bleak *BLEEK* ADJECTIVE

without warmth or cheer; gloomy [The *bleak* plain stretched on for miles into the distance.]

concoct *kun•KOKT* VERB

1. to come up with (something) by using a variety of things [Are you going to *concoct* one of your amazing fruit drinks?]

2. to make up; to think up [What excuse will Melvin *concoct* for being late this time?]

craze *KRAZE* NOUN

something that is extremely popular at the moment [That toy was the *craze* last year.]

impressionable *im•PRESH•un•uh•bul*

ADJECTIVE easily impressed or influenced [Many *impressionable* people who saw that ad bought the product.]

incompatible *in•kum•PAT•uh•bul* ADJECTIVE

not able to go together or get along together; not able to exist in harmony [Dogs and cats are often *incompatible* animals.]

obsession *ub•SESH•un* NOUN

1. anything that one thinks or worries about constantly or much too much [Howie has an *obsession* with beating Shabaz in the pole vault competition.]

2. a feeling that one needs to perform some action over and over, without good reason [She has an *obsession* with washing her hands; she does it about fifty times a day.]

partition *par•TISH•un*

VERB to divide into parts [A new wall was built to *partition* the room.]

NOUN something that separates a space into parts, such as a wall [The *partition* dividing our room was a blanket hung from the ceiling.]

presumptuous *pree•ZUMP•choo•us*
ADJECTIVE

wrongly assuming that one is equal, accepted, or welcome; too confident; bold in an unthinking way [It was *presumptuous* of Erin to show up uninvited and expect us to give her dinner.]

repulsive *ri•PUL•siv* ADJECTIVE

very unpleasant to the senses, feelings, or thoughts; disgusting [Bradley's Halloween monster mask was really *repulsive*.]

shortcoming *SHORT•kum•ing* NOUN

a falling short of what is expected or needed; a weakness or fault [Being forgetful is a *shortcoming* of his that creates many problems.]

solicit *suh•LISS•it* VERB

to try to get (something) by asking [We went to the mall to *solicit* signatures on the petition.]

stagnant *STAG•nunt* ADJECTIVE

1. foul due to lack of motion [The bad smell from that *stagnant* pond will ruin our picnic.]

2. not active; not brisk [In a *stagnant* housing market, few people buy homes.]

unfounded *un•FOWN•did* ADJECTIVE

not based on fact or reason [Mrs. Wallace's distrust is *unfounded*; I've never lied to her.]

Still Unfounded

A hiker got lost in the woods. After wandering for days, exhausted and starving, she was thrilled to see a forest ranger coming toward her. "Thank goodness," the hiker exclaimed. "I've been lost for three days, and things were starting to look bleak!"

"Three days? Why, that's nothing!" scoffed the ranger. "I've been lost for four weeks!" ■

Exercise A: If...
Write the Word that best completes each sentence.

USE A WORD ONLY ONE
TIME IN EACH EXERCISE.

1. If you tend to believe what you're told, do what others suggest, and are greatly affected by what you see and hear, you are . . . . _____

2. If you and your cousin argue constantly, don't enjoy the same things, and get on each other's nerves, you two are . . . . _____

3. If you react to something by saying "Ugh!" or "Yuck!" it's because you find this thing to be . . . . _____

4. If you can't get something out of your mind, and you talk about it, write about it, and dream about it, you have an . . . . _____

5. If you take it for granted that people want to see you, so you just show up places without being invited, you are . . . . _____

Exercise B: Mini-Rhyme Time
Write the Word that best completes each rhyme.

6. When people build a new section on a house and then make it into two rooms, they ___ the addition. _____

7. People who crawl into tight spaces are ___ to get trapped. _____

8. Seven days of boring gray skies would be a ___ week. _____

9. An easily clogged sink would be a ___ in the plumbing. _____

10. Someone who collects crystal likes to ___ glass. _____

Exercise C: What Is It?
Write the Word that each clue describes.

11. People may do this by going door-to-door requesting donations. _____

12. This can be a product everyone wants or a style everyone follows. _____

13. This describes colors that clash and people who quarrel constantly. _____

14. This could make you do things that aren't really logical or practical. _____

15. This describes the water in a swamp but not the water in a waterfall. _____

16. You do this to a stew when you create it with some of this and some of that. _____

17. Teenagers show that this word describes them when they imitate their heroes' behavior. _____

Exercise D: Synonyms

Write the **Word** that could be used in place of each underlined word or phrase.

18. That car's tiny trunk is a major <u>flaw</u> in its design.

_____

19. That conclusion is <u>not supported</u>, so why do you assume it is true?

_____

20. We have to <u>invent</u> a believable story to get Antonia here for her surprise party.

_____

21. Wearing brightly colored socks became a <u>fad</u> at our school.

_____

22. Through hard work, she was able to <u>save up</u> a huge fortune.

_____

23. The air in the closed-up room was <u>stale and still</u>, so we opened the windows.

_____

24. This food is simply <u>gross</u>, and I can't manage to swallow one bite.

_____

25. I thought it was <u>pushy</u> of Stuart to assume that we'd give him a ride.

_____

26. Nothing serves as a <u>divider</u> between the dining area and the living room.

_____

27. The window offered only a <u>depressing and bare</u> view of a windswept parking lot.

_____

28. Ahmad's remark was totally <u>appropriate</u>; he always knows just what to say.

_____

29. We need to <u>request</u> help from the entire neighborhood to get the park cleaned up.

_____

Exercise E: Antonyms

Write the **Word** that is an antonym for each set of words.

30. logical; sound; justified

_____

31. energetic; lively; fresh

_____

32. bright; rosy; exciting

_____

33. join; combine; unite

_____

34. slow; dumb; clumsy

_____

35. humble; timid; shy

_____

Criminal Obsession

Sherlock Holmes and his friend Dr. Watson were camping in the English countryside.

In the middle of the night, Holmes woke up Watson and said, "Look up, and tell me what you see."

Yawning, Watson replied, "The moon."

"What does that tell you?" asked Holmes.

Exercise F: Fill-in

Write the **Word** that best completes each sentence.

36. In the 1920s, short hair for women was the _____, and most "modern" young ladies got a short cut.

37. There is always someone trying to _____ spare change from people just coming out of that store.

38. If I find that my roommate and I are _____, will I be able to move to a different room?

39. That advertisement's claim is _____; there's no research at all to back up what it says.

40. Drapes were rigged up to _____ the backstage area into dressing rooms for the actors.

41. If you ask me, it was _____ of Ernestine to act as if everyone would want to sit next to her.

42. My dog is so _____ at picking up new tricks that it takes only a few minutes to teach her one.

43. The _____ look on Leon's face made me realize he did not feel hopeful about what would happen.

44. Business is _____ around here during the winter, but it picks up when tourists arrive in warm weather.

45. Miguel had to _____ an enormous quantity of note cards before he felt ready to start writing his research paper.

46. My neighbor has an _____ about cleanliness; she gets upset if the entire house isn't spotless.

47. His table manners are so _____ that I can't bear to watch him eat.

48. Young children are much more _____ than adults, but most of them eventually learn to judge things for themselves.

49. Let's put our heads together and try to _____ a plan that will succeed.

50. Elsie's unwillingness to try anything new is a _____ in her character.

"Oh. Er, I suppose it means that we are apt to have another nice day tomorrow," Watson said, barely able to keep his eyes open. "That conclusion may, of course, be unfounded. What does it tell you?"

"Elementary, Watson. What it tells me is that someone has stolen our tent." ■

"Indeed," Watson grumbled, "and while you amass clues, the chances are bleak hat I shall get any more sleep."

Quick LIST	amass V.	impressionable ADJ.	repulsive ADJ.
	apt ADJ.	incompatible ADJ.	shortcoming N.
	bleak ADJ.	obsession N.	solicit V.
	concoct V.	partition V., N.	stagnant ADJ.
	craze N.	presumptuous ADJ.	unfounded ADJ.

Lesson 4

affluence *AF•loo•unce* NOUN

wealth [George's huge home and fancy car are signs of his *affluence*.]

contaminate *kun•TAM•uh•nate* VERB

to make impure by adding something harmful or unwanted [If that chemical gets into the water supply, it will *contaminate* it.]

empathy *EM•puh•thee* NOUN

the ability to imagine what someone else is feeling [Having misplaced my own wallet, I had *empathy* for Darla when she lost hers.]

fallible *FAL•uh•bul* ADJECTIVE

capable of being mistaken; not perfect [Mr. Helm is usually right, but even he is *fallible*.]

---

infer *in•FUR* VERB

to understand or figure out, based on evidence; to conclude by the use of reasoning [No one came right out and said it, but I could *infer* from my classmates' remarks that they didn't like my short story.]

NOTE: What a person infers may or may not be correct. The more solid the evidence is and the better one's reasoning is, the greater are a person's chances of inferring correctly.

NEIGHBOR: Why did you infer that your new farm hand doesn't know anything about farming?

FARMER: Well, for one thing, he found some old milk bottles under the porch and told me he'd spotted a cow's nest.

"Well, don't have a cow!. Everyone's fallible."

measly *MEEZ•lee* VERB

very small or inferior; not enough [I think two dry little crackers is a *measly* snack.]

passive *PASS•iv* ADJECTIVE

acted upon without taking action in return; not resisting; taking no active part [The boy was surprisingly *passive* as the others teased him.]

proximity *prox•IM•uh•tee* NOUN

nearness [The Samuelsons didn't buy the house because of its *proximity* to a noisy airport.]

recoil *ri•KOIL* VERB

to draw back or shrink back in surprise, fear, or disgust [The sight of a spider on my pillow made me *recoil*.]

reputable *REP•yuh•tuh•bul* ADJECTIVE

having a good reputation; worthy of respect [A *reputable* plumber won't cut corners or overcharge you.]

scrounge *SKROUNJ* VERB

1. to get or find by hunting around; to scrape together [We went up to the attic to *scrounge* costumes for the play.]

2. to get by begging [He's hoping to *scrounge* some change from people passing by.]

sodden *SOD•un* NOUN

filled with moisture; soaked [My clothes were *sodden* after I got caught in that rainstorm.]

stench *STENCH* NOUN

a disgusting smell [Even closing the windows didn't protect us from the hog farm's *stench*.]

tirade *TY•rade* NOUN

a long and angry speech [The angry customer let loose with a *tirade* about the poor service.]

unprovoked *un•pruh•VOKED* ADJECTIVE

without cause; without having been brought about by an action [The man told the police that he had not said or done anything, that the attack on him was *unprovoked*.]

Exercise A: Put It Briefly
Write the **Word** that best completes each sentence.

USE A **WORD** ONLY ONE
TIME IN EACH EXERCISE.

1. A good detective doesn't depend only on stated information but also uses clues, interprets behavior, "reads between the lines," and "puts two and two together." *Briefly*, a detective is able to ___ things. _____

2. No one had made dinner, and we were hungry; we found crackers in the pantry, located some cheese in the fridge, and discovered a few apples in a basket. *Briefly*, to eat, we needed to ___. _____

3. Opening her three presents, Gina found a plastic necklace with a broken clasp, a check for one dollar, and a mitten (yes, just one). *Briefly*, all of Gina's gifts were ___. _____

4. I have friends, but Juanita is new to our school and doesn't know anyone; I think that would be scary, and I sense her loneliness and can relate to her situation. *Briefly*, what I'm experiencing is ___. _____

5. Dee's Dog Walking Service has been doing a good job for a long time; everyone who has used it knows that it's honest, responsible, dependable, and worth the cost. *Briefly*, the company is ___. _____

6. At the back of the theater, you can't hear the actors; at the middle, you hear better; and in front of the stage, you hear perfectly. *Briefly*, your ability to hear the actors is based on your ___ to them. _____

7. No matter how smart and careful people are, they're sure to make errors at one time or another because they're human, and all humans are wrong or inaccurate sometimes. *Briefly*, people are ___. _____

Exercise B: Synonyms
Write the **Word** that could be used in place of each underlined word or phrase.

8. Ricardo wrung out his <u>sopping wet</u> socks. _____

9. Dad delivered a <u>furious scolding</u> about my study habits. _____

10. Many people envied the man's <u>riches</u>. _____

11. Renee was surprised by Curt's <u>uncalled for</u> insults. _____

12. We were suddenly aware of a <u>horrible odor</u>. _____

13. Can't you react with <u>understanding</u> to my problem? _____

14. An oil spill can <u>pollute</u> miles of shoreline. _____

15. That source of information is <u>not always reliable</u>. _____

16. I need a <u>trustworthy</u> mechanic to work on my car. _____

Exercise C: True or False
Circle TRUE or FALSE for each statement.

STUDENT 1: My parents are sure to go into a tirade about my report card! Will yours?
STUDENT 2: Nah. My folks have too much on their minds to get upset about your grades.

17. Dropping a sandwich in a puddle would make it **sodden**. . . . . . . TRUE FALSE

18. Frosting on a cake **contaminates** it. . . . . . . TRUE FALSE

19. Rotten eggs and sour milk create a **stench**. . . . . TRUE FALSE

20. Watching TV is a **passive** way to spend time. . . . . . TRUE FALSE

21. An affectionate cat will **recoil** when you pet it. . . . . TRUE FALSE

22. When you **infer** something, you are always right. . . . . TRUE FALSE

Exercise D: Analogies
Write the letter of the word that completes the analogy.

_____ 23. *damp* : **sodden** :: *attractive* :
   A. ugly   C. beautiful
   B. pleasant   D. memorable

_____ 24. *skunk* : **stench** :: *rose* :
   A. thorn   C. blossom
   B. petal   D. fragrance

_____ 25. *spirited* : **passive** :: *rude* :
   A. sassy   C. loud
   B. polite   D. apologetic

_____ 26. *sob* : *sorrow* :: **tirade** :
   A. praise   C. displeasure
   B. surprise   D. amusement

Exercise E: Antonyms
Write the Word that means the opposite of each underlined word or phrase.

27. I'd be more comfortable with <u>distance</u> between us instead of such ___.

_____

28. They never <u>provide</u> a ride home but are always ready to ___ one.

_____

29. Francesca's fear that the dog would <u>pounce</u> made her ___.

_____

30. One customer left a <u>generous</u> tip; the other left a ___ one.

_____

31. Was Bernadette's response <u>justified</u> or ___?

_____

32. What good does it do to <u>hint</u> if you can't ___ what I'm getting at?

_____

33. I expected an <u>active</u> response to the news, but everyone was ___.

_____

34. In the city, there was evidence of both <u>poverty</u> and ___.

_____

35. First, <u>disinfect</u> the wound; then be careful not to ___ it again.

_____

Exercise F: Fill-in
Write the Word that best completes each sentence.

36. I doubt that my answer is wrong, but I'm _____, so it's possible that it is.

37. Hospitals must be careful not to let germs _____ the operating rooms.

38. The hotel is right downtown, and its _____ to stores and restaurants makes it a good place to stay.

39. My parents are searching for a _____ construction company to build an addition to our house.

40. Claudia's anger seemed _____ since I hadn't seen anything happen to make her so mad.

41. The guinea pig would _____ when I came near its cage; it wasn't eager to be picked up.

42. The front yard was _____ this morning because I forgot to turn off the sprinkler last night.

43. Flora showed her _____ by patting Anton's hand and asking if she could help.

44. We were able to _____ up some driftwood from the beach to make a campfire.

45. During Vance's _____, he banged his fist on the table and got quite red in the face.

46. Our neighbor's _____ is due to her having inherited several million dollars.

47. Don't be so _____ about life; get out there and do something to make things better!

48. You might _____ from the old clothes Mrs. Chen wears that she's poor, but she isn't.

49. Wally's _____ salary doesn't provide enough income to pay his rent.

50. A _____ coming from the henhouse made people hold their noses as they walked by.

FRIEND: How's your uncle doing with his dairy farm?
NIECE: Well, from what I can infer, he is a long way from affluence. Milk prices are so measly that it isn't worth milking the cows. And egg prices are worse; he can't afford to feed the chickens. He has to scrounge for every penny.
FRIEND: What's he doing about it?
NIECE: I don't know, but if it were my farm, I'd try to find something else for the cows and chickens to do!

NIECE: I think he ought to move the cows into the henhouse and send the chickens across the road.

Quick LIST

affluence N.	**fallible** ADJ.	**passive** ADJ.	**reputable** ADJ.	**stench** N.
contaminate V.	**infer** V.	**proximity** N.	**scrounge** V.	**tirade** N.
empathy N.	**measly** V.	**recoil** V.	**sodden** N.	**unprovoked** ADJ.

Lesson 5

abashed *uh•BASHD* ADJECTIVE

uneasy and somewhat ashamed of oneself [Melissa was *abashed* by Ken's kindness to her after she had been rude to him.]

balmy *BALL•mee* or *BAH•mee* ADJECTIVE

mild, pleasant, and gentle; *used in describing weather* [I sat on the shore, enjoying a *balmy* breeze off the lake.]

camaraderie *kam•uh•RAH•dur•ee* NOUN

a feeling of friendship, loyalty, and goodwill [The team members developed a great deal of *camaraderie* during the long season.]

dawdle *DAWD•ul* VERB

to waste time on unimportant things or by being slow [We can finish the hike in an hour if no one *dawdles*.]

Two women in a busy café wait impatiently to be served. When a waiter finally appears, they order coffee. "Don't dawdle," one woman adds, "and make sure the cup is clean."

A few minutes later the waiter returns with their coffee. "Okay," he says, "now which one of you gets the clean cup?" ∎

irk *URK* VERB

to annoy or irritate [After a while, Izzy's habit of whistling softly really began to *irk* me.]

manifest *MAN•ih•fest*

ADJECTIVE clear and evident; obvious [Lisa shook with *manifest* anger over the insult.]

VERB to make clear or reveal; to be evidence of [Rattlesnakes *manifest* their presence with an unmistakable noise.]

onslaught *ON•slot* NOUN

a violent and intense attack [The soldiers tried to prepare for the coming *onslaught*.]

proponent *pruh•POH•nunt* NOUN

one who actively supports a cause or idea [My uncle is a *proponent* of stricter laws for protecting the environment.]

relevant *REL•uh•vunt* ADJECTIVE

connected or related to what is being discussed or considered [The facts about an event are *relevant* to a news story; the reporter's opinion about the event is not.]

retort *ri•TORT*

VERB to reply quickly or sharply [If anyone criticizes Mel, he always *retorts* with some kind of insult.]

NOUN a sharp or witty reply [Samuel Johnson, who wrote the first real English dictionary, was famous for coming up with good and often funny *retorts*.]

severity *suh•VAIR•uh•tee* NOUN

1. strictness; harshness [We knew that Dale would be punished, but the *severity* of the punishment shocked us.]

2. seriousness [The length of a prison term is usually based on the *severity* of the crime.]

3. sharpness, intensity, or violence [When the storm increased in *severity*, it was reclassified as a hurricane.]

squander *SKWON•dur* VERB

to spend or use foolishly and wastefully [Every week, Ilyana *squanders* her allowance on magazines and video games.]

testy *TESS•tee* ADJECTIVE

easily irritated or annoyed [Juliane was a little *testy* this morning, so I kept out of her way.]

unerring *un•AIR•ing* or *un•UR•ing* ADJECTIVE

completely accurate; making no mistakes [Alonzo has an *unerring* sense of what colors look good together.]

vanquish *VANG•kwish* VERB

to defeat thoroughly; to win a victory over [For many years, the power of the Roman Empire allowed it to *vanquish* all its enemies and conquer a huge territory.]

Exercise A: Rhyme Time

Write the **Word** that best completes each rhyme.

1. He's not a very pleasant guest. He
   Grumbles, snarls, and seems quite ___.

   _____

2. During the test, do not let your mind wander.
   Time, at such times, isn't something to ___.

   _____

3. Just one sniff and I know what my mother's preparing.
   My nose for what's cooking is sharp and ___.

   _____

4. Jill bragged that she could jump the curb. Instead, she crashed.
   And then she looked both battered and ___.

   _____

Exercise B: If . . .

Write the **Word** that best completes each sentence.

5. If your mother shakes her head and frowns and glares at you when you do something, and there's absolutely no mistaking how she feels, her disapproval is . . . .

   _____

6. If someone says something mean to you, and you immediately fire back a clever remark in answer, then what you say is a . . . .

   _____

7. If money just "burns a hole in your pocket," and you buy things you don't really need, and you have no savings at all, then money is something you . . . .

   _____

8. If it's not too hot and not too cold, and the air feels soft and soothing, and being outside is just a delight, the day is . . . .

   _____

9. If you are studying the Civil War, your teacher might encourage you to read novels or watch movies set during the war because what you learned from them would be . . . .

   _____

10. If you stop and smell the roses and watch a grasshopper and look for four-leaf clovers while you're walking to school, you . . . .

    _____

11. If an emergency room is very crowded, and not everyone can get treated immediately, the doctors will treat people's injuries and illnesses in order of their . . . .

    _____

12. If you're part of a group of people you enjoy being with, and you'd help them any time they needed it, you're experiencing . . . .

    _____

13. If you bumped against a bee hive, and several hundred bees came swarming out of it and buzzed around you and stung you, that would be a kind of . . . .

    _____

Exercise C: Synonyms

Write the **Word** that is a synonym for each set of words.

14. apparent; plain; unmistakable   _____

15. backer; enthusiast; defender   _____

16. grumpy; grouchy; touchy   _____

17. overcome; conquer; beat   _____

18. sure-fire; perfect; faultless   _____

19. lag; putter; fool around   _____

20. bother; pester; bug   _____

Exercise D: Antonyms

Write the **Word** that is an antonym for each set of words.

21. hurry; hustle; rush   _____

22. soothe; please; comfort   _____

23. opponent; enemy; critic   _____

24. save; preserve; hold onto   _____

25. bitterness; hatred; conflict   _____

26. gentleness; mildness; weakness   _____

27. unimportant; beside the point; unrelated   _____

Exercise E: What Is It?

Write the **Word** that each clue describes. This exercise continues on the next page.

28. During a war or a football game, this
    is what one side tries to do to the other.   _____

29. This describes a short-tempered person.   _____

30. This describes more days in Hawaii than in Alaska.   _____

31. When children do this rudely, it's called "talking back."   _____

32. You do this to someone when you get on that person's nerves.   _____

33. If you forgot your best friend's birthday, this is how you'd feel.   _____

CUSTOMER: Waiter, do you have wild duck?
WAITER: No, but I can take a calm one and irk it for you.

CUSTOMER: I'll have the oysters, but they must not be too big or too tough, and I want them sweet, fresh, and fast.
WAITER: Certainly. And do you want them with or without pearls?

CUSTOMER: There are manifestly far too many roaches in this café!
WAITER: No, I believe I can say unerringly that we have only as many as the city allows.

"I'm already a little irked about being on the menu!"

34. This occurred repeatedly at the Alamo and on D-Day during World War II, and many times in many other wars. _____

35. You could do this to your reaction to food by making a face when you taste it. _____

Exercise F: Fill-in

Write the **Word** that best completes each sentence.

36. Worry and a lack of sleep had made Mom _____, and she snapped at everyone who tried to help fix breakfast.

37. Patrick Henry made it clear that he was a _____ of American independence in his "Give me liberty or give me death" speech.

38. One factor that helped the Spanish to _____ the Aztecs was superior weaponry.

39. The day of the picnic was clear and _____, and we were all relieved.

40. Clara's errors on the test were _____ to the conversation she was having with her parents about her grades.

41. A bloodhound's _____ nose allows it to track one particular person, even though many people may have crossed the path.

42. My brother's _____ when I said he was driving me crazy was "Well, *that's* a short trip!"

43. Rita was _____ by her classmates' loud laughter when she thought she had given the right answer.

44. The _____ of the rules and discipline at Jake's house make it hard for him to get away with anything.

45. My sisters _____ so much every morning that Mom has to get them up an hour earlier than me.

46. Joe tried not to _____ his boredom by yawning, but the dull lecture made it hard to hide his reaction.

47. Interrupting people tends to _____ them, especially if you do it repeatedly.

48. To prepare for the hurricane's _____, townspeople boarded up windows and stocked up on candles and batteries.

49. There was such a great feeling of _____ in our cabin at summer camp that we felt as if we'd been friends for years.

50. Our family has enough money if we don't _____ any of it; but if we aren't careful, we'll run short.

Quick LIST

abashed ADJ.
balmy ADJ.
camaraderie N.
dawdle V.
irk V.
manifest ADJ., V.
onslaught N.
proponent N.
relevant ADJ.
retort V., N.
severity N.
squander V.
testy ADJ.
unerring ADJ.
vanquish V.

Testy Retorts

CUSTOMER: Waiter, your thumb is sticking in my steak!

WAITER: Yes, I didn't want it to fall on the floor again.

CUSTOMER: This isn't fit for a pig!

WAITER: Indeed, sir? I'll go find you something that is!

Word Fun 1!

Word Fun answers start on page 150.

Defining

Match the invented word to its meaning.

_____ 1. *camarobbery*

_____ 2. *extraineous*

_____ 3. *knockturnal*

_____ 4. *laughluence*

_____ 5. *padestal*

_____ 6. *relephant*

A. a cushioned base

B. a rich sense of humor

C. friendship among thieves

D. what an unneeded locomotive is

E. what a rap on the door at midnight is

F. what Dumbo's remarks are when he sticks to the subject

Digging

Each sentence suggests a **Word** from Unit 1. The word itself is buried in the sentence. Find that word and underline it. In the example, the hidden word is *fabricate*. The words you need to dig up are *infer, renown,* and *sedate.*

Example: If I put a tack in this <u>fabric at e</u>ach corner, I can attach it to the window frame to make a shade.

1. No one said to plant the seeds in fertile soil, but I guessed it from other things that were said.

2. In her usual calm and unemotional way, she used a term that was very proper.

3. They have become so famous that they are now noticed everywhere they go.

Rhyming

These poems are pretty bad. To make them better, substitute a **Word** from Unit 1 for the underlined words so that the lines rhyme and have a regular rhythm.

1. The blanks I couldn't fill in on the test
   Made my lack of study <u>obvious and clear</u>. _____

2. When I dropped my mother's china and it smashed,
   She was mad and I was quite
      <u>embarrassed and ashamed</u>. _____

3. My brother is so lazy that if someone mentions toil,
   He's sure to gasp with horror and is likely to
      <u>shrink backwards</u>. _____

4. Don't jostle the hive or you'll anger the bees,
   And they will be awfully hard to
      <u>soothe and make peaceful</u>. _____

ASK THE ZOOKEEPER

Dear Z.K.:
The Siberian tiger at the zoo reminds me of my cat Ruby. She used to sit beside a plant on a pedestal on my porch, but one day she fell off and came down right on her head. Cats do *not* always land on their feet, I guess!

Anyway, the thing is this: If I can induce Ruby to stand on a scale, she weighs eight pounds. If she wants to be picked up, she weighs almost nothing. If she doesn't want to be picked up, I could just as well be trying to lift a sodden Siberian tiger out of a stagnant swamp. How can a cat be so light one day and so heavy the next?

Eulalie Throckmorton

Dear E.T.:
Are you sure it was Ruby who fell on her head?

Crossing

Across

1. This is like pity, and when you feel it, you know what someone else is going through.

4. This is a leaning—for or against. Referees and judges should not have it.

7. Collectors do this to the things they collect.

9. If you do this when you should hurry, you'll be late.

10. Things that get on your nerves do this to you.

12. This describes wise, clever people. It's what you'd want your lawyer to be.

13. This means to bring on, cause, or persuade, and it rhymes with *moose*.

14. A smart aleck is usually ready to use this as a reply.

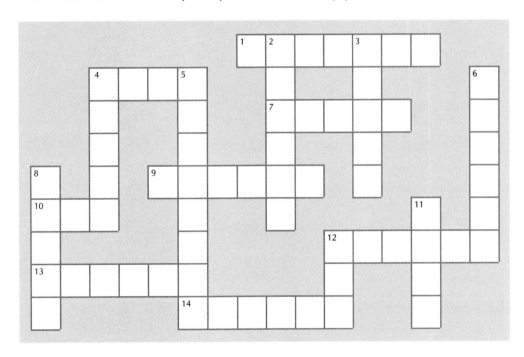

Down

2. If this describes something, it's not enough or not good enough.

3. You feel this way when you get up on the wrong side of bed.

4. This describes gray, cloudy days and hopeless attitudes.

5. If you use money (or time or whatever) wastefully, you do this to it.

6. This is a speech from someone who is angry and goes on and on about it.

8. This is the kind of watch kept by a night watchman, guard dog, or nurse.

11. This could describe thick grass or luxurious surroundings.

12. This can mean "likely" or "quick to learn."

Lesson 6 _____

abrasive *uh•BRAY•siv*

ADJECTIVE **1.** able to scrape or wear away by rubbing; rough; coarse [Falling on the *abrasive* surface of the sidewalk skinned Luke's knee.]

ADJECTIVE **2.** harsh or rough in quality [Her *abrasive* personality offends many people.]

NOUN a substance used to rub, scrape, grind, or polish [Toothpaste contains a mild *abrasive* that helps clean and polish teeth.]

benevolent *buh•NEV•uh•lunt* ADJECTIVE

inclined to do good; kind; generous [All over town, *benevolent* people donated canned goods for the food drive.]

compulsory *kum•PUL•sur•ee* ADJECTIVE

required; necessary [We have a system of *compulsory* education in this country.]

deft *DEFT* ADJECTIVE

neat and quick; skillful [Lester scooped up the ball with a *deft* motion, making it look easy.]

frustrate *FRUSS•trate* VERB

1. to block an effort to reach a goal; to defeat or make useless [Rain would *frustrate* our efforts to have the party outside.]

2. to cause to feel discouraged and unable to succeed [Trying to tie your shoes while wearing mittens will just *frustrate* you, so take the mittens off!]

impetuous *im•PECH•oo•us* ADJECTIVE

acting hastily and with sudden feeling rather than with thought or planning [Don't lose your temper and do something *impetuous*.]

outgrowth *OUT•growth* NOUN

something that grows out of something else, either physically or as a result [My friendship with Debra was an *outgrowth* of our working together on the play last spring.]

precarious *pri•KAIR•ee•us* ADJECTIVE

not safe or secure; dangerous [The roof's slippery surface made it a *precarious* place for anyone to try to work.]

priority *pry•OR•uh•tee* NOUN

1. the state or fact of being earlier in time [The settler put markers on the land to establish the *priority* of his claim.]

2. something that is given, or is worthy of being given, more or earlier attention [Mom says my safety and happiness are both important, but her main *priority* is my safety.]

reimburse *ree•im•BURCE* VERB

to pay back money spent or to repay for loss, damage, or expenses [Ben says if I lend him five dollars, he'll *reimburse* me Monday.]

saunter *SAWN•tur* VERB

to walk in a casual and unhurried way [I watched Sharon *saunter* away as if she didn't have a care in the world.]

subside *sub•SIDE* VERB

1. to sink to a lower level or become less [The flood waters slowly began to *subside*.]

2. to quiet down or become less active [Lou let his anger *subside* before he gave a reply.]

tumult *TOO•mult* NOUN

1. the noise and confusion of a crowd [The *tumult* in the gym meant the game had begun.]

2. a feeling of confusion and disturbance [Mary couldn't make a decision while her mind was in such *tumult*.]

veer *VEER* VERB

to change direction; to turn [Leo had to *veer* suddenly to avoid an oncoming car.]

vivacious *vi•VAY•shus* ADJECTIVE

full of energy; lively [Wesley's *vivacious* storytelling kept us all interested.]

PRIORITIES

Deep inside a great, magical forest, a lever stuck up from the earth. At first glance, one might have thought it was some peculiar outgrowth of a root, for   many mighty trees grew up close around it.

But this was a magic lever. Pushing it would trigger the end of the world.

Exercise A: Put It Briefly

Write the Word that best completes each sentence.

USE A WORD ONLY ONE TIME IN EACH EXERCISE.

1. In a busy emergency room, the quickest and most dramatic efforts are made for patients most in need of treatment, who receive care first. *Briefly*, these patients have . . . .

   _____

2. The increase, over time, in the height of the average person is a natural development that is due to healthier food and more of it. *Briefly*, it's an ___ of better nutrition. . . . .

   _____

3. Harriet was extremely upset; her feelings were in such a jumble of anger, fear, and annoyance that she simply couldn't think straight. *Briefly*, her mind was in a . . . .

   _____

4. When you're riding your bike and someone gets in your way, you can't keep going straight; you need to steer to one side or the other. *Briefly*, you must . . . .

   _____

5. Math problems that I don't understand upset and irritate me because I think that I will never get them right, and I just want to quit trying. *Briefly*, they ___ me. . . . .

   _____

6. Chandler was impatient and unwilling to think things through, so he made a quick, reckless decision without considering the consequences. *Briefly*, his decision was . . . .

   _____

7. The picnickers were spirited and bouncy and cheerful and busy and bright and full of motion and activity. *Briefly*, they were . . . .

   _____

8. My mom said if I buy milk, she'll give me back what it cost so the expense isn't really mine. *Briefly*, she will ___ me. . . . .

   _____

9. The doctor put a breathing tube down the patient's throat rapidly and without any awkwardness. *Briefly*, the action was . . . .

   _____

Exercise B: What Is It?

Write the Word that each clue describes.

10. An example of this is sandpaper. _____

11. A branch or twig is this, and so is a wart.

    _____

12. This is what the earliest request for something has.

    _____

13. This describes something you have no choice about doing.

    _____

14. An inability to find a mailbox would do this to your efforts to mail a letter.

    _____

One day a wandering foreigner sauntered down the seemingly abandoned road that curved through the forest. Nathan was a person who took "scenic" routes to avoid the tumult of the busier highways.

He was also a person who could never let his curiosity be frustrated. So when he saw the odd lever, he had to find out what it did.

Exercise C: Synonyms

Write the Word that could be used in place of each underlined word or phrase.

15. The trapped animal's struggles began to <u>decrease</u> as it became exhausted. _____

16. My balance on the narrow beam was <u>unsteady</u>, so I was quite nervous. _____

17. The boys made the car wait for them to <u>stroll</u> lazily across the intersection. _____

18. Many <u>big-hearted</u> people contributed to the earthquake survivors' fund. _____

19. Increased sales of fans is a predictable <u>consequence</u> of hot weather. _____

Quick LIST

abrasive ADJ., N.
benevolent ADJ.
compulsory ADJ.
deft ADJ.
frustrate V.
impetuous ADJ.
outgrowth N.
precarious ADJ.
priority N.
reimburse V.
saunter V.
subside V.
tumult N.
veer V.
vivacious ADJ.

Exercise D: Matching

Match each phrase on the left to the phrase on the right that means the same, or nearly the same, thing.

_____ 20. very **vivacious**   A. considerable commotion

_____ 21. **benevolent** boss   B. positively peppy

_____ 22. readily **reimburse**   C. swerve sharply

_____ 23. tremendous **tumult**   D. risky route

_____ 24. abnormally **abrasive**   E. rapidly refund

_____ 25. certainly **subside**   F. charitable chief

_____ 26. **precarious** path   G. strangely scratchy

_____ 27. **veer** violently   H. definitely decrease

Of course, Nate didn't know the world's fate hung precariously on one impetuous push of a lever.

Suddenly a car zipped around a curve. The driver quickly saw that she must make a terrible decision: (a) run over the man in the middle of the road; (b) veer to the left, hit the lever, and end the world; or (c) veer to the right, crash into a tree without hitting the man or the lever but likely killing herself!

In an instant, she recognized her priorities and ran over Nate.

Question:
Was it the right decision? Why?

Exercise E: Antonyms

Write the Word that means the opposite of each underlined word or phrase. This exercise continues on the next page.

28. Is our attendance at practices <u>voluntary</u> or ___? _____

29. One singer's voice was <u>smooth</u>; another's was ___. _____

30. I'm so <u>clumsy</u> at this; how did you get to be so ___ at it? _____

31. Wendy is usually <u>cautious</u>, so her ___ action totally surprised us. _____

32. The wind and rain will <u>intensify</u> before the storm begins to ___.   _____

33. When I'm in a hurry, I <u>run</u>, but when I just want to enjoy the outdoors, I ___.   _____

34. Ramps <u>help</u> people in wheelchairs get around, but curbs tend to ___ their efforts.   _____

35. The <u>calm</u> of the country road contrasted with the ___ of rush hour that I was used to.   _____

Exercise F: Fill-in

Write the Word that best completes each sentence.

36. _____ to the right when you come to the fork in the road.

37. Brian likes to _____ around town and see what's going on.

38. The theater erupted in _____ when someone yelled "Fire!"

39. Felipa used her allowance to _____ the library for the book she had lost.

40. Len's anxiety about the exam began to _____ as his studying showed how well he knew the material.

41. Coretta's interest in becoming a vet is a logical _____ of her love of both animals and science.

42. Kendra was shy and quiet at first but became more _____ as she got to know us.

43. "Look before you leap" is good advice, but Tod is too _____ to follow it.

44. Studying three years of a foreign language is _____, but we can choose which language to take.

45. A puzzle that is too difficult will just _____ a five-year-old instead of being fun.

46. Homework is considered a _____ at our house, and I can't watch TV until it's done.

47. I need something _____, such as scouring powder, to really get the sink clean.

48. With one _____ flick of the wrist, Dad sent his fishing line sailing into the stream right where he wanted it.

49. The king, a _____ ruler, did his best to increase his people's happiness and well-being.

50. The ladder's _____ position on the porch step made me more than a little nervous.

Answer: Yes, because better Nate than lever!

Lesson 7 _____

aghast *uh•GAST* ADJECTIVE

struck with amazed dismay; shocked and astonished [Amelia was *aghast* at the sight of the wreck.]

curt *KURT* ADJECTIVE

so short or brief as to seem rude [Shu Nan's reply to my invitation was a *curt* "No."]

disarray *dis•uh•RAY* NOUN

1. an untidy condition; disorder or confusion [After Mom and Dad's anniversary party, our house was in complete *disarray*.]

2. disorderly dress [I threw on some clothes and arrived on time but in a state of *disarray*.]

extrovert *EX•truh•vurt* NOUN

a sociable person who likes to be with other people and makes friends easily [One reason that Mr. Herrera is such a good salesman is that he's an *extrovert*.]

finagle *fi•NAY•gul* VERB

to get or arrange by cleverness or trickery; to use sneaky methods [Eli used a slight sniffle to *finagle* his way out of doing his work.]

immoral *ih•MOR•ul* ADJECTIVE

not moral; wrong according to the standards of right and wrong; sinful [Andy felt guilty about cheating, knowing that it was *immoral*.]

improvise *IM•pruh•vize* VERB

1. to perform without preparation [Sergio can *improvise* a clever song on any subject.]

2. to make from whatever is available [Let's try to *improvise* a raft from the driftwood we find on the beach.]

outlandish *out•LAN•dish* ADJECTIVE

very odd; extremely strange [Ivan has the *outlandish* idea that the squirrels in the back yard are trying to communicate with him.]

overcast *OH•vur•kast* ADJECTIVE

cloudy (said of the sky or the weather) [An *overcast* day is predicted for tomorrow.]

pittance *PIT•unce* NOUN

a very small allowance, wage, or payment [The workers claimed they were receiving only a *pittance* for their long hours of labor.]

quell *KWEL* VERB

1. to bring to a stop; to put an end to (something) by force or persuasion; to overcome [The police tried to *quell* the riot quickly and without injuries to anyone.]

2. to make calm; to quiet [The mother talked gently to her son to *quell* his fear.]

recur *ri•KUR* VERB

to happen or occur again [If those strange noises from last night *recur* tonight, I'm going to try to find out what's causing them.]

shirk *SHIRK* VERB

to avoid or leave undone (something that should be done) [You can always count on Yazmina; she won't *shirk* her obligations.]

unswerving *un•SWUR•ving* ADJECTIVE

1. not turning aside or changing course [The bull made an *unswerving* charge across the pasture, straight for the red pickup.]

2. steady; firm; not changing [Even when times were hard, my parents' devotion to each other was *unswerving*.]

There once was a fellow named Irving,
Whose energy Irv was conserving.
  He was able to shirk
  Nearly all of his work;
Irv's devotion to sleep was unswerving!

vogue *VOHG* NOUN

1. the fashion or style at a particular time [Both short hair and short skirts were the *vogue* for women in the 1920s.]

2. popularity or general acceptance, usually of a temporary nature [I wonder what colors will be in *vogue* this year.]

Exercise A: *If...*
Write the Word that best completes each sentence.

USE A WORD ONLY ONE
TIME IN EACH EXERCISE.

1. If you scheme and plan and plot and use crafty methods to get something you want, what you do is to .... _____

2. If something is widely accepted now as a way to dress or to act or to decorate a home, but it hasn't always been, it's currently in ...... _____

3. If it's about two o'clock in the afternoon, and you're in an open field but have no shadow, the day is probably .... _____

4. If someone is the life of the party and enjoys mixing with others and exchanging ideas, that person is an .... _____

Exercise B: Rhyme Time
Write the Word that best completes each rhyme.

5. I'd hoped for praise when I so proudly served him my dessert,
   But all he said was "I've had worse," and that, I thought, was ___. _____

6. Fritz was chosen captain, and he was the most deserving,
   His dedication to the team was solid and ___. _____

7. The house burned to the ground so fast
   That we could only watch, ___. _____

8. I need a new alarm clock to be sure
   My tardiness today does not ___. _____

9. If you don't have the right supplies,
   You just might have to ___. _____

10. My dad said, "Put your things away.
    I'm sick of all this ___!" _____

Outlandish

Exercise C: True or False
Circle TRUE or FALSE for each statement.

11. Cruelty is considered to be *immoral*. .... TRUE FALSE

12. Cough syrup is used to help *quell* a cough. .... TRUE FALSE

13. People are usually delighted to earn a *pittance*. .... TRUE FALSE

14. *Extroverts* tend to be shy and fearful of strangers. .... TRUE FALSE

15. What is in *vogue* can change from one year to the next. .... TRUE FALSE

16. One who accepts an assignment should be sure to *shirk* it. .... TRUE FALSE

17. Learning from a mistake decreases the chances that it will *recur*. .... TRUE FALSE

Exercise D: Antonyms
Write the Word that means the opposite
of each underlined word or phrase.

18. Walter is a <u>loner</u>, but Maxwell is the kind of ___ who loves to meet new people.

_____

19. After our long trip, Jenny's <u>neatness</u> was a sharp contrast to my wrinkled ___.

_____

20. Can't Mary Ann ever behave in a <u>normal</u> way instead of doing such ___ things?

_____

21. My new salary seemed like a <u>huge amount</u> compared to the ___ I got at my last job.

_____

22. Laughing at Tomasina will only <u>intensify</u> her anxiety, not ___ it.

_____

23. Al ran in a <u>dodging and twisting</u> way, but Barry's run was ___.

_____

24. Elsa's response was <u>polite and gracious</u>, but Cathy's was ___.

_____

25. We had hoped for a <u>sunny</u> day, but it was ___.

_____

Exercise E: Synonyms
Write the Word that could be used in place
of each underlined word or phrase.

Aghast?

26. My dog's loyalty is <u>strong and constant</u>.

_____

27. One can't rely on people who <u>neglect</u> their duties.

_____

28. Is that kind of shirt the <u>very latest thing</u> this winter?

_____

29. It took the king only two days to <u>crush</u> the rebellion.

_____

30. Carla wouldn't shoplift; she knows that stealing is <u>wicked</u>.

_____

31. When we saw the damage left by the tornado, we were <u>horrified</u>.

_____

32. If you'd just pay attention, this kind of problem wouldn't <u>come up from time to time</u>.

_____

33. Yoshi, Joanne, and I had to <u>make up, on the spot,</u> a short skit about pioneer life.

_____

34. Zoe wasn't on the guest list, but she managed to <u>slyly acquire</u> an invitation to the party.

_____

35. My three-year-old sister, who had dressed herself, was wearing a really <u>weird</u> outfit.

_____

Exercise F: Fill-in

Write the **Word** that best completes each sentence.

Quick LIST

aghast ADJ.
curt ADJ.
disarray N.
extrovert N.
finagle V.
immoral ADJ.
improvise V.
outlandish ADJ.
overcast ADJ.
pittance N.
quell V.
recur V.
shirk V.
unswerving ADJ.
vogue N.

36. Hoping to _____ a raise in her allowance, Aggie claimed she always spent all her money on school supplies.

37. We decided to _____ a casserole out of anything we could find in the cupboard.

38. How could Stanley _____ his responsibility to the team by missing every practice?

39. Dark red lipstick was the _____ last year, but more natural tones are "in" now.

40. The classroom was in such _____ that it looked as if a hurricane had passed through it.

41. Can people really survive on the _____ those factory employees receive for their work?

42. After he realized what he'd done was _____, his conscience really started to bother him.

43. Romeo and Juliet's love would have been _____, I think, even if they had lived for many years.

44. The drapes were open, but the day was so _____ that the room was dim without the lights on.

45. I tried to chat with Stefan, but his _____ replies to my questions did not encourage conversation.

46. Rowena has never been a real _____; she prefers to spend time alone with her music.

47. Habits are behaviors that _____ so often that one does them without even thinking.

48. Why did Jean get that _____ haircut that's so much longer on one side than the other?

49. The vet tried to _____ the gerbil's nervousness by stroking it and talking in a soothing voice.

50. Kate was so _____ at the size of the car repair bill that she was speechless.

Occur

Recur

Exercise G: Writing

Think of what things are in **vogue** right now—in clothes, hair, architecture, car design, music, computer games, movies, TV shows, and so on. On your own paper, use TWO or more **Words** to describe one of those things. Also explain why you think it's so popular and your own feelings about it.

Lesson 8 _____

allegation al•uh•GAY•shun NOUN

a formal, but not yet proved, accusation [Armand's *allegation* that I stole money from the club treasury is totally untrue!]

animosity an•uh•MOSS•uh•tee NOUN

obvious anger or hatred [There is no excuse for showing *animosity* toward members of the other team.]

befitting bee•FIT•ing ADJECTIVE

appropriate to; suitable or proper for [That outfit is more *befitting* a casual picnic than a formal dance.]

brevity BREV•uh•tee NOUN

shortness of time; briefness [After so many months, I was glad to see my aunt but sorry about the *brevity* of our time together.]

curtail kur•TAIL VERB

to put limitations on; to cut short; to reduce [Having little money will definitely *curtail* our activities this weekend.]

deface dee•FACE VERB

to damage or spoil the surface or appearance of [A child's crayon marks can *deface* a wall.]

frivolous FRIV•uh•lus ADJECTIVE

not very important or serious [My cousin is always interested in *frivolous* things like what the latest fashions are.]

impart im•PART VERB

1. to give or add something, such as a quality [Using a flute always seems to *impart* cheerfulness to a melody.]

2. to give information or knowledge [Please *impart* to Helen the time of the meeting.]

oppression uh•PRESH•un NOUN

1. the act of keeping down by unjust use of power [Thomas Jefferson and many others objected to England's *oppression* of the American colonies.]

2. a sense of being heavily weighed down or troubled [The heat and humidity created an *oppression* that made it hard to work.]

peevish PEEV•ish ADJECTIVE

easily annoyed [The children were *peevish* because they missed their nap.]

proficient proh•FISH•unt ADJECTIVE

very capable; quite able [A *proficient* writer, Frankie always gets excellent grades on his research papers.]

regress ri•GRESS VERB

to go back; to move backward; to return to an earlier condition or behavior [Problems at home made the seven-year-old *regress*, and she went back to sucking her thumb again.]

stodgy STAH•jee ADJECTIVE

dull or uninteresting due to being overly traditional or formal; boringly old-fashioned [My uncle is much too *stodgy* to even listen to the kind of music I like, much less dance to it!]

totality toh•TAL•uh•tee NOUN

the condition or fact of being complete or total; the total amount [We need to consider the problem in its *totality* in order to figure out how best to deal with it.]

unkempt un•KEMPT ADJECTIVE

untidy in a way that results from neglect [Your hair is looking pretty *unkempt* today.]

Question: What is Japan more proficient at producing than any other country?
Answer: Japanese people

Question: How might people impart messages to each other deep in the forest?
Answer: by Moss Code

Exercise A: Mini-Rhyme Time
Write the **Word** that best completes each rhyme.

USE A WORD ONLY ONE TIME IN EACH EXERCISE.

1. Destructive people who throw paint on a room's walls ___ the space. _____

2. A useful bag that is worthy of holding the scarf a lady is making is one ___ her knitting. _____

3. A charge that a country has broken an international law is an ___ against a nation. _____

4. A company that can't afford what it has been spending on postage may have to ___ its mail. _____

5. To think about every part of a girl's nature and all of her individual qualities would be to consider the ___ of her personality. _____

Exercise B: Opposites
They say that opposites attract, and these couples are good examples. Complete the sentence about each couple with a **Word**.

6. Bonnie cooks badly, clogs up the vacuum cleaner, and smears the windows. At domestic chores, however, Ronnie is ___. _____

7. Morris is lively, amusing, bright, and bouncy. He loves to have fun, take chances, and try new things, and he's about as up-to-date as anyone can be. Doris, however, is ___. _____

8. Pearl is cheerful, even-tempered, patient, and agreeable. No matter what happens, she deals with it in a pleasant way. It seems that nothing upsets her. Earl, however, is ___. _____

9. Farrell makes changes that are for the better and sticks to them. He keeps on going and making progress. After a few days of improvement, however, Cheryl is likely to ___. _____

10. Manny shaves every morning, gets regular haircuts, uses his brush and comb often, sews missing buttons on his clothes, and irons his shirts. Fannie, however, is ___. _____

11. Trudy goes on and on and *on* when she talks. She is chatty, gabby, and long-winded. She takes forever to say anything. Rudy's remarks, however, are known for their ___. _____

Exercise C: What Is It?
Write the **Word** that each clue describes. This exercise continues on the next page.

12. Patients do this when they start to get better, then get worse again. _____

13. This is stated when a person is arrested and charged with a crime. _____

14. You'd want to find this quality in a speech that bored you.   _____

15. Sudden bad weather might do this to a camping trip.   _____

16. Graffiti and vandalism do this to property.   _____

Exercise D: Yes or No

Circle YES or NO for each statement.

17. Would putting a spice in a stew **impart** a flavor to it? . . . .   YES   NO
18. Are you happy to see people toward whom you feel **animosity**? . . . .   YES   NO
19. Would an old barn be a place **befitting** a conference of world leaders? . . . .   YES   NO
20. Are debts and overdue bills likely to give a person a feeling of **oppression**? . . . .   YES   NO
21. Does a lawn look **unkempt** when it is overgrown and full of weeds? . . . .   YES   NO
22. Would a **stodgy** party be likely to keep all the neighbors awake? . . . .   YES   NO
23. Is an Olympic gold medalist **proficient** at his or her sport? . . . .   YES   NO

Exercise E: Synonyms

Write the Word that is a synonym for each set of words.

24. carefree; silly; light   _____

25. messy; rumpled; sloppy   _____

26. ill will; bitterness; dislike   _____

27. professional; qualified; expert   _____

28. mistreatment; persecution; abuse   _____

29. tell; pass on; communicate   _____

30. irritable; touchy; grouchy   _____

31. entirety; wholeness; sum   _____

Exercise F: Other Forms of Words

Use what you know about the Words to choose the correct answers. This exercise continues on the next page.

_____ 32. Taxes would be considered **oppressive** if they were
  A. very high.   B. not adequate.   C. urgently needed.

_____ 33. If what a boy does **peeves** you, you'd be most likely to
  A. thank him.   B. avoid him.   C. try to help him.

Dr. Kato and Dr. Sato shared offices. Although serious and proficient at their work, the two dentists tended to be rather frivolous in their tastes and hoped to move to new, less stodgy offices.

One day Dr. Kato said, "Dr. Sato, I have found a space befitting both the importance of our work and our pleasingly light-hearted approach to it!"

"Splendid, Dr. Kato!" said Dr. Sato. "I have felt an oppression here that, I must admit, has made me peevish. Where is It?"

"On the river, Dr. Sato!" said Dr. Kato. "It is a boat!"

"Marvelous, Dr. Kato!" said Dr. Sato, and they soon began to fix up the

Quick LIST

allegation N.
animosity N.
befitting ADJ.
brevity N.
curtail V.
deface V.
frivolous ADJ.
impart V.
oppression N.
peevish ADJ.
proficient ADJ.
regress V.
stodgy ADJ.
totality N.
unkempt ADJ.

_____

boat, giving extra effort to imparting a sense of fun to its decoration. They even hired a captain to sail it up and down the river while they saw patients.

On opening day, Dr. Kato and Dr. Sato happily stepped out onto the dock to hang their new sign. A model of wit and brevity, it said: "TOOTH FERRY." ∎

"Cool!" said Dr. Kato.
"In totality!" said Dr. Sato.

_____ 34. A day of *frivolity* might include a visit to
    A. a prison.   B. a lecture.   C. an amusement park.

_____ 35. If you *allege* that a woman committed a crime, you are saying
    A. she did it.   B. she's innocent.   C. you have proof.

Exercise G: Fill-in

Write the Word that best completes each sentence.

36. His study habits improved, but he began to _____ after a while and was soon back to his old, lazy ways.

37. Buying fashion magazines seems to be a _____ use of money when there isn't enough food in the house.

38. Our family's new budget requires us to _____ our expenses.

39. Photographs of the boss's family _____ a warmth to his office.

40. The cats showed such _____ toward each other that I feared they would fight.

41. Dad looked _____ after a week of camping, but with a shower and fresh clothes, he was his normal, tidy self again.

42. Jilana is _____ in both Italian and English, having lived for long periods in both Italy and Britain.

43. The _____ of the Russian people by the czars eventually led to the Russian Revolution.

44. Don't _____ the library books by writing in them or underlining passages.

45. Luca was _____, snapping at me about every little thing; I guess he got up on the wrong side of bed.

46. Due to the _____ of our coach's instructions, we didn't need all the time allowed during our time out.

47. The mayor denied the _____ that she had accepted bribes while in office.

48. I wanted to dress in a way _____ the occasion, but I really couldn't afford anything new.

49. We soon realized that Yolanda was just too _____ to lighten up and get into the spirit of the party.

50. Although each task was a simple one, the _____ of the effort was huge because there were so many tasks.

Lesson 9

acclaim *uh•KLAIM*

VERB to greet with loud approval; to praise with enthusiasm [The audience cheered to *acclaim* the band's performance.]

NOUN very high praise [The man's heroism earned him national *acclaim*.]

cringe *KRINJ* VERB

to draw back from something that is painful, unpleasant, frightening, or dangerous [A puppy is likely to *cringe* if an older dog growls and snaps at it.]

deluge *DEL•yooj*

NOUN **1.** a very heavy rainfall [The forecast warned of a *deluge* that could flood the area.]

NOUN **2.** an overwhelming rush of anything [The factory had to hire more workers to deal with a *deluge* of orders.]

VERB **1.** to flood [A tidal wave can *deluge* a seacoast.]

VERB **2.** to overwhelm [Fans began to *deluge* the star with autograph requests.]

envision *en•VIZH•un* VERB

to form a mental picture; to imagine [It's hard to *envision* Uncle Jasper as a goofy teenager.]

horrendous *hor•REN•dus* ADJECTIVE

horrible; terrible [I'm not surprised that café closed; the food and service were *horrendous*.]

invaluable *in•VAL•yuh•bul* ADJECTIVE

having a value so great that it cannot be measured; extremely valuable [Having a friend to talk to in tough times is *invaluable*.]

nurture *NUR•chur* VERB

to help someone or something grow and develop [We tried to *nurture* Jerry's talent by sending him to a good theater school.]

prohibitive *proh•HIB•uh•tiv* ADJECTIVE

likely to prevent [LuWanda has a roommate because the cost of living alone is *prohibitive*.]

quandary *KWON•dree* NOUN

a condition of confusion or doubt due to being faced with a difficult situation [Ashley was in a *quandary* when the bus left without her.]

regal *REE•gul* ADJECTIVE

characteristic of, or suitable for, a king or queen; splendid and dignified; royal [The hotel's ballroom has a *regal* magnificence.]

scapegoat *SKAPE•goat* NOUN

one who is blamed, or takes the blame, for the wrong actions of another [Robbie was often the *scapegoat* for his brothers' misbehavior.]

skulk *SKULK* VERB

to move about in a sneaky way in order to remain hidden or unnoticed [If you see anyone *skulk* around our house while we're away, would you call the police?]

The burglar used trees as a screen
In an effort to get away clean.
But he had too much bulk
To successfully skulk,
And he couldn't avoid being seen.

tart *TART* ADJECTIVE

1. a sharp or sour taste [The dish was served with a really *tart* sauce that made my mouth pucker.]

2. sharp in tone or meaning [Aunt Louise's *tart* remark about my muddy shoes sent me scurrying to take them off.]

unwary *un•WAIR•ee* ADJECTIVE

not aware of danger; not watchful or cautious [The dishonest store owner cheated *unwary* customers out of thousands of dollars.]

versatile *VUR•suh•til* ADJECTIVE

1. having many different skills or talents [Mara is a *versatile* performer who can sing, dance, and act.]

2. having many uses [A cowboy's neck scarf is a *versatile* item; it can serve as a dust mask, handkerchief, or bandage, as well as a scarf.]

Exercise A: Put It Briefly

Write the Word that best completes each sentence.

USE A WORD ONLY ONE
TIME IN EACH EXERCISE.

1. Yesterday when my buddy broke a window and ran, I got nabbed; when the dog ate a box of cookies, Mom assumed I had done it; when my sister tracked dirt all over the living room, Dad yelled at me. *Briefly,* yesterday I was a . . . .

   _____

2. More and more letters poured in, arriving in bags and bins until they covered every table and desk and spilled onto the floor, where they piled up in stacks and heaps. *Briefly,* the mail became a . . . .

   _____

3. In responding, the woman's voice was crisp and brisk, with an edge to it; she made a pointed remark that let everyone know she wasn't going to put up with any nonsense. *Briefly,* her reply was . . . .

   _____

4. My uncle made rules including no snacks before dinner; no TV or piano playing; no feet on the couch; no exploring in the attic; no handling of tools; and no yelling. *Briefly,* all his rules were . . . . . .

   _____

Exercise B: Antonyms

Write the Word that is an antonym for each set of words.

5. limited; narrow; specific   _____

6. mild; mellow; sweet   _____

7. careful; suspicious; alert   _____

8. worthless; unimportant; useless   _____

9. wonderful; excellent; superb   _____

10. restrict; neglect; harm   _____

*A Sprinkle
of Questions*

1. What do criminals do when a city is deluged?
2. What happened to the river during the deluge?
3. How do you know when a deluge is going to be really, really bad?
4. After an area has been totally deluged, where is the water the deepest?

Exercise C: Synonyms

Write the Word that could be used in place of each underlined word or phrase. This exercise continues on the next page.

11. I was impressed by the <u>noble and majestic</u> way she carried herself.

    _____

12. Don't <u>shrink away</u> when the horse nuzzles you; he won't bite you.

    _____

13. If I see a man <u>creep</u> down a dark alley, I figure he's up to no good.

    _____

14. This handy, <u>multipurpose</u> tool can help with many repair jobs.

    _____

15. A clear, detailed description helps listeners <u>visualize</u> a scene.

    _____

16. Ralph told me about the <u>predicament</u> he found himself in. _____

17. She set a trap to catch the next <u>unsuspecting</u> passerby. _____

18. The firefighters' brave efforts deserve our <u>applause</u>. _____

19. Your loyalty and help are <u>very precious</u> to me. _____

Nature nurtures.

20. We saw a <u>dreadful</u> traffic accident. _____

Exercise D: Questions
Write the Word that best answers the question.

Nurture nature.

21. What kind of residence is a palace? _____

22. What do gardeners do to young plants? _____

23. What does camouflage clothing help a soldier do? _____

24. What kind of price keeps you from making a purchase? _____

25. What will a lake do to the area near a dam if the dam breaks? _____

26. What are you in when you're in a pickle, a jam, or hot water? _____

27. What do you do to something if you see it in your "mind's eye"? _____

28. What do people often do when they are splashed with icy water? _____

29. What kind of person can build houses, write songs, and make pie? _____

30. What's the word for someone who is seen as being guilty but isn't? _____

Exercise E: Analogies
Write the letter of the word that completes the analogy.

_____ 31. *drizzle* : **deluge** :: *murmur* :
   A. shout   B. giggle   C. secret   D. trickle

_____ 32. **acclaim** : *boo* :: *give* :
   A. send   B. praise   C. donate   D. receive

_____ 33. *move* : **skulk** :: *listen* :
   A. hear   B. speak   C. whisper   D. eavesdrop

_____ 34. *valuable* : **invaluable** :: *afraid* :
   A. shy   B. unafraid   C. terrified   D. concerned

_____ 35. *sweet* : *fudge* :: **tart** :
   A. salt   B. sugar   C. lemon   D. watermelon

Horrendous Answers to a Sprinkle of Questions:

1. They go on a crime wave.

2. It got too big for its bridges.

3. Sparrows start sandbagging their nests.

4. At the bottom

Exercise F: Fill-in

Write the Word that best completes each sentence.

36. The pickpocket was successful in stealing from _____ people in the crowd.

37. The man's request was pleasant, but something _____ in his manner made me feel he was used to being instantly obeyed.

38. The sharp sound of a car backfiring made me _____ and look around in momentary panic.

39. Sara gazed at the store display, trying to _____ how the skirt would look with her favorite sweater.

40. Cameron's training as a lifeguard was _____ when his friend fell overboard while they were sailing.

41. If the time required were not so _____, Mia would take the train across the country instead of flying.

42. I don't understand the critics' _____ for that film; I found it boring and ridiculous.

43. Alana found herself in the _____ of not knowing whom to trust or where to turn for help.

44. The coach became the _____ for the team's losses even though he wasn't to blame.

45. Good parents _____ their children's minds as well as their bodies.

46. If customers _____ the store with complaints, maybe that rude clerk will get fired.

47. I bought a _____ kitchen gadget that chops, grinds, and mixes food.

48. Rachel's _____ reply to my repeated questions showed her irritation and impatience.

49. Foxes _____ around the chicken coop at night, but they never show up during the day.

50. The _____ battle that took place at Shiloh was one of the worst in the Civil War.

"My regal throat hurts! Where are my [Cough!] cough drops? I want my mommy!"

Question:
What is it when a regal person has a sore throat and starts acting like a whiny little crybaby?

ʞɔǝu ǝɥʇ uı
uıɐd lɐʎoɹ ∀
:ɹǝʍsu∀

Quick LIST

	envision V.	**prohibitive** ADJ.	**skulk** V.
acclaim V., N.	**horrendous** ADJ.	**quandary** N.	**tart** ADJ.
cringe V.	**invaluable** ADJ.	**regal** ADJ.	**unwary** ADJ.
deluge N., V.	**nurture** V.	**scapegoat** N.	**versatile** ADJ.

You already know how to pronounce and use these familiar words. Now learn some of their less-familiar meanings.

angle VERB

to use tricks or sly methods to try to get something [Denzel is sure to *angle* for an invitation to Holly's party.]

balance NOUN

the part left over; remainder [I got some of my allowance, and I'll get the *balance* tomorrow.]

charge

VERB to give instructions to; to command [If the captain *charges* us to retreat, we'll do so.]

NOUN **1.** someone or something that is put in someone's care [The babysitter kept a close eye on her *charges* at the playground.]

NOUN **2.** care and protection [I won't leave my cats in the *charge* of anyone I don't trust.]

composed ADJECTIVE

calm and self-controlled; not confused or excited [Imelda seemed quite *composed* while she waited to give her speech.]

cow VERB

to frighten; to take away one's spirit or make timid [You can shake your fist at me all you like, but you're not going to *cow* me.]

distant ADJECTIVE

1. related, but not closely [I met some *distant* cousins at the family reunion.]

2. not actually rude but not at all friendly; indicating cool feelings [Alex's *distant* nod made me wonder if he'd heard my criticism.]

gravity NOUN

the condition of being important, serious, or solemn [Josh's worried look made it clear that he realized the *gravity* of the circumstances.]

Out in a pasture:

MADGE: Isabel, everyone else in the herd is in a panic about mad cow disease! How can you stay so composed?

ISABEL: Why should I get upset over some stupid cow disease? I'm a jet airplane! Zoom! Zoom! Zoom!

harbor VERB

1. to provide a place of protection for (someone); to hide (someone) in order to protect him or her [Any person who knowingly *harbors* a criminal can get into serious trouble.]

2. to hold in one's mind; to mentally hold on to [Daphne says she won't cheat anymore, but I *harbor* some suspicions of her.]

lumber VERB

to move along heavily, often in a clumsy, slow, or noisy fashion [The truck shifted gears as it began to *lumber* up the hill.]

mad ADJECTIVE

1. crazy; insane [Everyone thought the old man was *mad* when he claimed to be the king.]

2. wildly excited; unable to think clearly; frantic [The mother was *mad* with fear until her lost child was found.]

3. devoted to in an excitedly enthusiastic way [That couple is just *mad* about each other.]

reflect VERB

1. to think carefully and seriously [I need to *reflect* on all the choices before I decide.]

2. to show, display, or demonstrate [Chester hoped his paper would *reflect* all the time and effort he had spent on it.]

spruce ADJECTIVE

neat, clean, simple, and correct in appearance [Richard looked quite *spruce* in his uniform.]

stir NOUN

a state of excitement [The news that a Hollywood star would visit the school created a *stir*.]

untold ADJECTIVE

too many or to great to be counted, measured, or accurately described [That statue honors soldiers' *untold* sacrifices for the nation.]

wasted ADJECTIVE

weakened; feeble; worn away [Maria's battle with pneumonia had left her *wasted*.]

Exercise A: Put It Briefly

Write the Word that best completes each sentence.

USE A WORD ONLY ONE
TIME IN EACH EXERCISE.

1. Emilia was hired to feed, water, and walk her neighbor's dog, watch out for it, and deal with any problems that might come up. *Briefly*, the dog was Emilia's ___.

   _____

2. Hippopotamuses are not dainty or highly flexible animals. They weigh a great deal, and their legs are short and thick, so motion requires real effort. *Briefly*, when hippos walk, they ___.

   _____

3. We were shocked by Dean's appearance. Hard work and a shortage of rest and food had taken his strength, and he was thin and exhausted. *Briefly*, Dean looked ___.

   _____

4. A salesman should be tidy and well-dressed. His hair should be trimmed; his clothes should be fresh and ironed; his shoes should be shined. *Briefly*, the salesman should be ___.

   _____

5. Vicky wants more money but won't ask for it. Instead, she will flatter her boss, show off her best work, and hint about other job offers she has received. *Briefly*, Vicky will ___ for a raise.

   _____

6. Despite the danger, Enrico seemed undisturbed. He showed no signs of being upset, was in complete command of his actions, and kept his head. *Briefly*, Enrico was ___.

   _____

7. The dog allowed me to pet him, but he didn't wag his tail and soon turned away. I snapped my fingers and whistled, but he simply ignored me. *Briefly*, the dog was ___.

   _____

8. Suzanne paid part of her credit card bill. She didn't pay it all, but she will next month. Her paycheck will cover every last cent that she still owes. *Briefly*, Suzanne will pay the ___.

   _____

Exercise B: Matching

Match each phrase on the left to the phrase on the right that means the same, or nearly the same, thing.

MADGE: *Isabel, I don't think you see the gravity of this situation!*
ISABEL: *Not from this altitude! Zooooom!*

_____ 9. ***cow*** a companion   A. a disturbance at the depot

_____ 10. a ***stir*** in the station   B. fantastically fond of food

_____ 11. ***mad*** about mealtime   C. a dignified delegate

_____ 12. ***lumber*** along the lane   D. in the kids' keeping

_____ 13. in the children's ***charge***   E. trudge up the trail

_____ 14. a ***composed*** congressman   F. bully a buddy

Exercise C: Synonyms

Write the Word that could be used in place of each underlined word or phrase.

15. I was embarrassed by Nan's <u>chilly</u> response to my happy greeting.   _____

16. The earthquake killed or injured <u>countless</u> thousands of people.   _____

17. The judge will <u>order</u> the jury to consider all the evidence.   _____

18. Natalie will <u>try to scheme</u> to get free tickets to the show.   _____

19. <u>Consider</u> for a moment—do you really want to do this?   _____

20. Can you finish the <u>rest</u> of the work tomorrow?   _____

21. Why do you <u>cling to</u> resentment toward me?   _____

Exercise D: Mini-Rhyme Time

Write the Word that best completes each rhyme.

Up in a jet:

WILLY: I'm always cowed by flying in these jumbo jets. I mean, how often do they crash?

BILLY: Once, I imagine.

22. A dentist soberly describing
    tooth decay would discuss a cavity with ___ .   _____

23. To mention a recent commotion is to refer to the ___ .   _____

24. A child's soiled clothing, dirty face, and snarled hair ___ neglect.   _____

25. Someone who can scare a girl has the power to ___ her.   _____

26. A young man who has lost his mind is a ___ lad.   _____

Exercise E: Antonyms

Write the Word that means the opposite of each underlined word or phrase. This exercise continues on the next page.

Later:

WILLY: Do cows fly?

BILLY: Are you mad?

27. They have <u>little</u> money now but once had ___ wealth.   _____

28. Proceed in a <u>calm, steady</u> manner; don't get into a ___ rush.   _____

29. I certainly wasn't expecting to hear such <u>merriment</u> in Dad's voice; I expected ___ .   _____

30. The long, hard day left Jameel <u>rumpled and grimy</u>, although he had left the house looking ___ .   _____

31. Our <u>strong, healthy</u> appearance contrasted with the ___ bodies of refugees in the camp.   _____

32. A panther and a lion are <u>close</u> relatives; a pet cat and a lion are more ___ relatives.   _____

33. A foreign government might <u>turn over</u> people accused of crimes in this country, or it might ___ them in its own.   _____

34. Georgette was able to <u>conceal</u> her lack of training for a while, but eventually her mistakes began to ___ it.   _____

35. Try to <u>scamper</u> down to first base, don't ___!   _____

Exercise F: Fill-in

Write the **Word** that best completes each sentence.

36. The boss's bad temper and harshness managed to _____ all his employees.

37. Mac was determined that every camper in his _____ would remain healthy and safe.

38. We ate all the peaches we could and saved the _____ of them for canning.

39. Caleb picked up the heavy box and started to _____ through the snow.

40. I think Tammy is annoyed with me; she acted so _____ all evening.

41. Brandon was anxious about whether he looked _____ enough for his job interview.

42. I don't know how Conchita could remain so _____ while everyone else was a nervous wreck.

43. The mood following the tragedy was one of _____; everyone spoke in low tones.

44. A bad call by the line judge produced a _____ among the spectators at the tennis match.

45. Mom told me to sit in my room and _____ on how I'd let the entire family down.

46. The actual result of any war is _____ misery for everyone involved in it.

47. Photographs showed the _____ bodies of those who stood in line for emergency food supplies.

48. I'll bet Glenda will _____ for a ride home by making somebody feel sorry for her.

49. The man was _____ with grief and did not seem to know what he was doing.

50. "Nations that _____ our enemies are enemies themselves," said the general.

_____

Quick LIST

angle V.
balance N.
charge V., N.
composed ADJ.
cow V.
distant ADJ.
gravity N.
harbor V.
lumber V.
mad ADJ.
reflect V.
spruce ADJ.
stir N.
untold ADJ.
wasted ADJ.

_____

Zoooom!

I'd never spied a
flying cow.
I never thought
I'd spy one.
I harbor no hard
feelings,
But I never want
to fly one!

Word Fun 2! _____

Boxing

Fill in each set of blanks with a word you know that matches the clue.
The boxed letters will spell out the answer to the question at the bottom.

1. Something that's in vogue for a short time . . . .

2. What you might use if your hair is unkempt . . . .

3. A word that means "to impart knowledge" . . . .

4. What money to be reimbursed is called . . . .

5. Drivers step on these when their speed becomes precarious . . .

6. What a scapegoat gets stuck with . . . .

7. The color of an overcast sky . . . .

Question: How does a hotdog speak?   Answer:

Mad but Unswerving

A man on the bus was complaining to a lady about the tumult at his home. "My three brothers and I live in one room," he said. "One brother has seven dogs, another has six cats, and the third has a baboon. The disarray, noise, and smell are horrendous!"

Envisioning the situation, the lady was sympathetic. "I don't know what you could do to quell the noise or prevent the mess," she said. "But, as for

Matching

Match each phrase on the left to the phrase on the right that means the same, or nearly the same, thing.

____ 1. a mad lad   A. come up with a costume

____ 2. a deft theft   B. praise the playing

____ 3. a regal beagle   C. picture a pile-up

____ 4. a spruce caboose   D. skillful stealing

____ 5. acclaim the game   E. a dignified dog

____ 6. envision a collision F. a tidy train car

____ 7. improvise a disguise G. a batty boy

Naming

Match each name below

____ 1. Kurt Ale

____ 2. Bea Fitting

____ 3. Vi Vayshus

____ 4. Annie Mossity

____ 5. Ally Gayshen

____ 6. Kwan Dree

____ 7. Finn Aygul

____ 8. Dee Face

Rhyming

Make each poem rhyme and have a poetic rhythm by substituting a **Word** from Unit 2 for the underlined words.

1. I was surprised, and my feelings were hurt
   When replies to my nice, friendly greetings
      were <u>so short as to be almost rude.</u>

   _____

2. Rocks below the surface make a warning necessary
   For they are quite a hazard to a diver
      who's <u>not alert to possible danger.</u>

   _____

the smell, can't you open a window?"

   The man looked at her, aghast. "What, and let all my birds escape?" ■

to the description it goes best with.

A. She's always making accusations.

B. No one's livelier or peppier than she.

C. She tends to clench her fists and snarl.

D. He's between a rock and a hard place.

E. She always dresses and behaves suitably.

F. This guy can shorten or reduce almost anything.

G. She always leaves scratches and dents on things.

H. He gets what he wants by cleverness and trickery.

Searching

Circle all the words you can find that go from left to right or from top to bottom. Among them, you'll find answers to the clues below.

U	K	I	M	E	S	S
P	C	T	O	P	F	T
Y	R	I	O	A	L	O
G	A	S	P	Y	O	P
L	N	I	E	A	O	T
A	K	N	N	W	D	U
D	Y	S	D	N	I	R
S	U	B	A	C	K	N

1. Where priorities are on a "to do" list

2. Where you go when you regress

3. What you might do if you're aghast

4. What you do when you veer

5. What immoral actions are

6. How a peevish person feels

7. Another word for *disarray*

8. Another word for *deluge*

Question:

When the deluge came, what happened to the cargo ship loaded with paint?

Answer: It got wrecked, and all the sailors were marooned!

Lesson 11

attire *uh•TIRE*

> VERB   to dress; to clothe   [I'm not sure how to *attire* myself for such a fancy party.]

> NOUN   clothes   [A torn T-shirt is not suitable *attire* for that restaurant.]

chronic *KRON•ik* ADJECTIVE

> **1.** lasting a long time or coming back again and again   [I've suffered from a *chronic* cold.]

> **2.** continual or done by habit   [Kevin whines all the time; he's just a *chronic* complainer.]

distort *dis•TORT* VERB

> **1.** to change from a natural shape   [A curved mirror *distorts* one's reflection.]

> **2.** to change from what is true; to fail to truly represent   [When you quote only part of what someone says, you may *distort* the meaning.]

docile *DOSS•ul* ADJECTIVE

> gentle, obedient, and trainable; easy to deal with   [Golden retrievers are active and energetic but *docile* dogs.]

doleful *DOLE•ful* ADJECTIVE

> full of sorrow or sadness   [With a *doleful* face, the boy watched his friend's family pack as they prepared to move across the country.]

fallacy *FAL•uh•see* NOUN

> **1.** a false or mistaken idea, belief, or opinion   [Columbus knew that the belief that the earth was flat was a *fallacy*.]

> **2.** an error in reasoning; incorrect reasoning   [Diego tried to point out the *fallacy* in Jeff's argument, but Jeff couldn't see it.]

fruitful *FRUIT•ful* ADJECTIVE

> producing results; successful   [A bake sale may be a *fruitful* way to raise the money we need.]

immobile *ih•MOH•bul* ADJECTIVE

> **1.** not movable   [Setting the fence posts into concrete will keep them *immobile*.]

> **2.** motionless; not moving   [It's best to remain *immobile* while you're getting a haircut.]

indignation *in•dig•NAY•shun* NOUN

> deep anger about something that seems wrong, unjust, or mean   [The accusation that he was lying filled Hector with *indignation*.]

ostracize *OSS•truh•size* VERB

> to exclude or keep out; to refuse to have anything to do with   [Larry knew that if he told on the other boys, they would *ostracize* him.]

pompous *POM•puss* ADJECTIVE

> showing too great an opinion of one's own importance; having an exaggerated idea of one's own dignity   [He's too *pompous* to allow anyone to call him by his first name.]

revoke *ri•VOKE* VERB

> to take back or bring to an end something that has been given or permitted, such as a right, agreement, or privilege   [Will the traffic court judge *revoke* Zeke's driver's license?]

snare *SNAIR*

> NOUN   a trap used to catch small animals or something that works as a trap by being tempting or attractive   [Police detectives used the precious gems as a *snare* to help them capture the burglar.]

> VERB   to catch in a snare or trap   [We must try to *snare* the fox that raids our chicken coop.]

splurge *SPLURJ*

> VERB   to spend freely or too freely; to be extravagant   [Jim decided to *splurge* and get the jacket he liked even though he didn't need it.]

> NOUN   wild spending; an unnecessary expense or luxury   [Staying in such a fancy hotel was a *splurge*, but we enjoyed it.]

wince *WINCE*

> VERB   to shrink or draw back slightly from something in disgust, pain, or fear   [Joey didn't cry, but he did *wince* when he got the shot.]

> NOUN   the act of wincing   [At the recital, I could see the piano teacher's *wince* each time a pupil hit the wrong key.]

Exercise A: Mini-Rhyme Time
Write the Word that best completes each rhyme.

1. Thorny branches will stop you if they ___ your hair.

2. A desire to overdo it with purchases is an urge to ___.

3. A duke who is totally paralyzed by fear is a truly ___ noble.

4. Nothing in my closet fits; I need to go shopping to acquire ___.

Exercise B: Antonyms
Write the Word that means the opposite of each underlined word or phrase.

How? Well, doc, there wath thith thnare out in the woodth, and my pal Tham thaid, "I dare you . . ."

Huh? But, doctor, if I keep my tongue immobile, how can I thpeak clearly?

5. The losing team was ___, but the winners were joyous.

6. Some of the children were ___; others were wild and uncontrollable.

7. I couldn't find a single ___ in Cal's thought process; it showed perfect logic.

8. Is this pain in your back a ___ problem, or is it temporary and infrequent?

9. Credit cards can ___ people into debts from which they cannot free themselves.

10. One side reacted to the verdict with ___, the other with pleased approval.

11. Dad decided to ___ my later curfew, but he will restore it if my grades improve.

Exercise C: What It Is Not
Write the Word that belongs in each blank.

12. A burro that bites, kicks, and refuses to move when it's supposed to is . . . . NOT

13. A man who is thoughtful and humble and modest is . . . . . . NOT

14. Elephants really do have very long memories; that is . . . . . . NOT a

15. Buying food and medicine for a sick, hungry child is . . . . . . NOT a

16. When a man who rarely lies does tell a lie, his lying is . . . . . NOT

17. When your efforts are useless and do no good, they are . . . . NOT

Exercise D: Synonyms

Write the Word that could be used in place of each underlined word or phrase.

18. The children were safe with the <u>tame and mild</u> pony.

_____

19. Marco spent quite a while choosing his <u>outfit</u> for the day.

_____

20. Any little pressure on my broken arm made me <u>flinch slightly</u>.

_____

21. The howling of the wolves sounded heart-breakingly <u>mournful</u>.

_____

22. Jose has <u>repeated</u> ear infections and must visit the doctor often.

_____

23. Alan's voice when he said "How _dare_ you!" showed his <u>outrage</u>.

_____

24. The cat sat completely <u>still</u> for so long that it looked like a statue.

_____

25. I think our efforts would be more <u>effective</u> if we worked together.

_____

26. Bret was able to <u>twist the meaning of</u> what I said by repeating only part of it.

_____

27. The government can <u>cancel</u> the passport of someone who is waiting to go on trial.

_____

28. In the rabbit's struggle to escape, the coiled vine worked as a <u>noose</u>, tightening around its leg.

_____

29. Because of the gossip, neighbors began to <u>reject and shut out</u> the entire family.

_____

Exercise E: If . . .

Write the Word that best completes each sentence.

If the stupid joke that used to be in this spot hadn't been _revoked_, it would have made you _wince_.

30. If you're afraid of toads because you think that touching one will give you warts, your fear is based on a . . . .

_____

31. If a man behaves in a "high-and-mighty," stuck-up, superior way and thinks he deserves great respect all the time, he is . . . .

_____

32. If you make a funny face by squinting and twisting your mouth down on one side and up on the other, your face is something you . . . . .

_____

33. If a sound really bothers you, such as fingernails on a blackboard or a high shriek, you would probably react with a . . . .

_____

34. If it is important that a table stay firmly in the same place so that it can't be budged, you might bolt it to the floor to make it . . . .

_____

35. If people turn their backs on Mr. X and won't include him in activities and act as if he doesn't exist, Mr. X is someone they . . . .

_____

Exercise F: Fill-in

Write the **Word** that best completes each sentence.

36. The _____ expression on Victor's face made me ask why he was so unhappy.

37. The speaker was so _____ that he expected everyone to stand up when he was introduced.

38. Great anger or pain can _____ a person's face, making it look quite different.

39. As long as the butterfly was _____, it was hard to see; but we all noticed it as it flew away.

40. Carl's voice was sharp with _____ when he objected to the way he'd been treated.

41. Joshua felt that a tie was a necessary part of his _____ for the job interview.

42. When Lee's friends hear what he did, will they _____ him and stop inviting him to do things with them?

43. Greg released a bird he had found caught in a _____ and watched it disappear among the trees.

44. Our fishing vacation was quite _____; we caught enough for several meals.

45. For weeks, Ray has had a _____ cough that just will not go away.

46. The paramedics had to _____ when they saw the accident victims' terrible injuries.

47. The high school will _____ the parking pass of any student whose car blocks the fire lane.

48. Matthew is a sweet, _____ little boy who does exactly what he's told to do.

49. If John continues to _____ on expensive clothes, his bank account will soon be empty.

50. It's a _____ that dogs have cleaner mouths than we humans do; their mouths just contain different germs.

Question: Is a dog better attired in summer or in winter?

Answer: Summer. A dog has a coat in the winter, but in the summer it has a coat and pants.

A man in Cleveland, Ohio, asks his doctor to advise him about his chronic weight problem.

The doctor says, "My guess is that you are too immobile. I think walking two miles a day may be fruitful exercise."

Months later, the man calls the doctor and says in a doleful voice, "Okay, I'm at the Atlantic Ocean. What now?" ∎

Quick LIST

attire V., N.	**docile** ADJ.	**immobile** ADJ.	**revoke** V.
chronic ADJ.	**doleful** ADJ.	**indignation** N.	**snare** N., V.
distort V.	**fallacy** N.	**ostracize** V.	**splurge** V., N.
	fruitful ADJ.	**pompous** ADJ.	**wince** V., N.

Lesson 12 _____

acquisition ak•wuh•ZISH•un NOUN
something acquired; something one gets or gains [We hadn't realized how much our lives would change with the *acquisition* of a puppy.]

admonish ad•MON•ish VERB
1. to scold gently [My dad is sure to *admonish* me if I use bad table manners.]
2. to caution, warn, or advise someone about his or her behavior or duties [Parents should *admonish* their children not to open the door to strangers.]

botch BOTCH
VERB to spoil by poor or clumsy work; to repair badly [If I try to fix the car myself, I may *botch* the job.]
NOUN a poor or clumsy piece of work [In her rush, Olive made a *botch* of fixing dinner.]

congenial kun•JEEN•yul ADJECTIVE
1. friendly, agreeable, and pleasant [I sat with a *congenial* girl who made me feel welcome.]
2. able to get along; having similar likes and dislikes [Luther and Ted are a *congenial* pair and do many things together.]

cope KOPE VERB
to deal with something successfully; to overcome difficulties [Mom sometimes finds it hard to *cope* with raising three children alone while she also has a job.]

deceptive di•SEP•tiv ADJECTIVE
misleading or deceiving or meant to mislead or deceive [The ice looked safe, but its appearance was *deceptive* because there were patches where it was very thin.]

detest di•TEST VERB
to strongly dislike; to hate [I *detest* that ugly shade of green.]

expertise ek•spur•TEEZ NOUN
the skill or special knowledge of an expert [Steve has developed real *expertise* as a cook.]

grim GRIM ADJECTIVE
1. appearing stern or harsh; cold and forbidding [When LaVon came home late, his father met him at the door with a *grim* face.]
2. not giving in; unyielding [With *grim* determination, the exploration party plodded on through the deepening snow.]
3. without hope; cheerless; depressing; gloomy [When Phil lost his job and his house burned down, life seemed quite *grim*.]

inhibit in•HIB•it VERB
to hold back; to hinder or make difficult [A sense of fairness should *inhibit* people from taking more than their share.]

lurch LURCH
VERB to move suddenly in an irregular and unsteady way; to suddenly roll, stagger, or rock [I caught my heel in the carpet, making me *lurch* into the room.]
NOUN a lurching movement [The roller coaster gave a *lurch* and then began to move more smoothly.]

nutritious nu•TRISH•us ADJECTIVE
providing the substances needed for growth and health [Candy bars may be delicious, but they do not make a *nutritious* meal.]

pang PANG NOUN
a sudden, sharp feeling of pain, either physical or emotional [When I landed, I felt a *pang* in my ankle.]

roundabout ROUND•uh•bout ADJECTIVE
not by the shortest route or quickest method; not direct [The main roads were clogged with traffic, so we had to take a longer, *roundabout* route to the shopping mall.]

unseemly un•SEEM•lee ADJECTIVE
not proper or decent; not in agreement with accepted standards of good taste [I stared at Maureen, shocked by her *unseemly* giggling during the memorial service.]

Exercise A: Matching

Match each phrase on the left to the phrase on the right that means the same, or nearly the same, thing.

USE A WORD ONLY ONE TIME IN EACH EXERCISE.

____ 1. *admonish* an advisor

____ 2. a *roundabout* route

____ 3. a *congenial* contributor

____ 4. essential *expertise*

____ 5. an acceptable *acquisition*

____ 6. *botch* the blending

____ 7. *inhibit* the inhabitants

____ 8. *lurch* to the left

A. restrict the residents

B. necessary know-how

C. a proper purchase

D. criticize a counselor

E. a winding way

F. sway sideways suddenly

G. mess up the mixing

H. a good-natured giver

Question:
What did the surgeon say to the patient after botching the operation?

Answer: "That is more than enough out of you!"

Exercise B: Synonyms

Write the Word that could be used in place of each underlined word or phrase.

9. Milk is one of the most <u>healthful</u> foods that people can consume, no matter what age they are.

_____

10. I believed Margie completely, not realizing that her description of what happened was <u>untrue</u>.

_____

11. Although their enemies were powerful, the soldiers fought on with <u>firm</u> courage.

_____

12. I suffered a <u>strong sensation of discomfort</u> of homesickness when I heard Mom's voice.

_____

13. It's hard to get children (or anyone else) to eat food that they <u>truly can't stand</u>.

_____

14. The train started forward with a <u>jerk</u>, and a standing passenger nearly landed in my lap.

_____

15. Sophie's parents always <u>caution</u> her to look both ways before she crosses any street.

_____

16. If Grandma has to live alone in that big house, I don't know how she can <u>manage</u>.

_____

17. After saving for years, my parents are ready to pursue the <u>ownership</u> of a home.

_____

18. Ned's way of solving the problem was <u>not the most efficient</u>, but he eventually got the answer.

_____

Exercise C: Antonyms

Write the Word that is an antonym for each set of words.

19. love; admire; adore

_____

20. fail; surrender; give up

_____

21. truthful; trustworthy; honest

_____

22. respectable; appropriate; dignified

_____

23. success; triumph; achievement

_____

24. encourage; permit; allow

_____

25. mean; cold; antisocial

_____

Exercise D: Rhyme Time

Write the Word that best completes each rhyme.

26. My life seems overwhelming. I just hope
    That I can somehow find the strength to ___.

_____

27. Was her behavior crude? I'd say, extremely!
    For everything she did was quite ___!

_____

28. The boat is sinking fast, and I have never learned to swim.
    I've got to say, right now, the future's looking pretty ___.

_____

29. The milk and mayonnaise are warm; the ice cubes will not freeze.
    We need a worker with refrigeration ___!

_____

Exercise E: Yes or No

Circle YES or NO for each statement.

30. Is it a good idea to ask for a raise on a day
    when your boss looks particularly **grim**? . . . .   YES   NO

31. Do **deceptive** ads give people a false impression? . . . . . .   YES   NO

32. Would people think it was **unseemly** for a
    man to remarry a week after his wife died? . . . .   YES   NO

33. Are doughnuts and a soft drink a **nutritious** meal? . . . . . .   YES   NO

34. Does a baseball card collector have an
    interest in the **acquisition** of baseball cards? . . . .   YES   NO

35. Is a person likely to enjoy experiencing a **pang**? . . . .   YES   NO

Quick LIST

acquisition N.
admonish V.
botch V., N.
congenial ADJ.
cope V.
deceptive ADJ.
detest V.
expertise N.
grim ADJ.
inhibit V.
lurch V., N.
nutritious ADJ.
pang N.
roundabout ADJ.
unseemly ADJ.

_____

Question:
When a girl slips
and falls on ice,
what inhibits her
brother from help-
ing her get up?

Answer: He can't
be a brother and
assist her too.

Exercise F: Fill-in

Write the Word that best completes each sentence.

36. Some senators claimed that higher import taxes would _____ international trade.

37. This highway will take you straight there, but the _____ route is prettier if you have time to take it.

38. People in the crowded refugee camp had a _____ existence, because food and medicine were so scarce.

39. A bowl of whole-grain cereal is even more _____ when you add fresh fruit to it.

40. Careless workers are more likely to _____ a job than careful workers are.

41. A wave made my little rowboat _____ to one side and threw me off balance.

42. The man's kindly attitude was _____, for he wanted to harm, not help, the stranger.

43. The eight travelers were a _____ group and enjoyed being together for the voyage.

44. Her main concern was the _____ of wealth, and she worked steadily to achieve it.

45. It was difficult for Bart to _____ with the demands of his job after a poor night's sleep.

46. Does that pilot have the _____ necessary to fly in these stormy conditions?

47. Parents should always _____ their children for failing to thank people for gifts.

48. Anna experienced a _____ of guilt about hurting her friend's feelings.

49. We thought it was _____ to be so high-spirited on the day of the tragedy.

50. I really, truly _____ the taste of that medicine and can hardly make myself swallow it.

Exercise G: Writing

What three things would you **admonish** people for or about? Do it now in THREE sentences, each using one Word. Think in terms of bad habits and annoying behaviors, but write advice that's good for everyone. Here's an example: "A simple question deserves a simple answer, not a long, *roundabout* explanation or opinion."

CUSTOMER (*left*): I'd like to try on that dress in the window.
CLERK (*right*): Okay, but surely it would be less unseemly if you used the dressing room like everyone else.

CUSTOMER: *Don't call me Shirley. I detest that.*

Lesson 13

align *uh•LINE* VERB

    1. to arrange or adjust in a straight line; to arrange things to be in the proper relationship with each other   [When parking a car, *align* the wheels with the curb.]

    2. to join or cooperate with others for or against a cause   [I'll *align* myself with the students who want a longer lunch period.]

conducive *kun•DOO•siv* ADJECTIVE

    to lead or contribute (to an effect)   [A gentle rocking motion is *conducive* to sleep.]

continuity *kon•tuh•NOO•uh•tee* NOUN

    the state of being unchanged over time   [An old mill on the river at the edge of downtown gave the town a feeling of *continuity*.]

daft *DAFT* ADJECTIVE

    extremely foolish or silly; crazy   [Ignore Mabel's latest idea; it is totally *daft*.]

> **Daft Poem 1**
>
> Excuse me, but I think it's daft
> To use concrete to make a raft.

epitome *ee•PIT•uh•mee* NOUN

    a person or thing that has all the typical qualities of something   [Her clothes are the *epitome* of good taste.]

facility *fuh•SIL•uh•tee* NOUN

    1. the ability to do something easily   [Basil has a *facility* for making friends.]

    2. equipment that makes some activity possible or easier; usually used in the plural   [Our school has the *facilities* for science lab work.]

    3. a building, room, or area for some activity [The city council voted to approve construction of the proposed new health care *facility*.]

gallivant *GAL•uh•vant* VERB

    to go here and there in search of amusement [My friends went out to *gallivant* around town, but I had to study.]

incredulous *in•KREJ•uh•luss* ADJECTIVE

    unwilling or unable to believe   [Ravi gave me an *incredulous* stare when I told him the news.]

jargon *JAR•gun* NOUN

    the special language used in a particular field of interest or activity   [In baseball *jargon*, a "rope" is a long line drive.]

mollify *MOL•uh•fy* VERB

    to make less angry   [Verleen tried to *mollify* the director by promising she'd never be late for rehearsal again.]

momentum *moh•MEN•tum* NOUN

    the force with which something moves   [The wagon gained *momentum* as it moved down the steep hill.]

repercussion *ree•pur•KUSH•un* NOUN

    something that happens as an effect of or reaction to an event or action; often used in the plural   [One of the *repercussions* of building so much new housing in our suburb has been overcrowded schools.]

> **Daft Poem 2**
>
> The revolution of the Russians Had some nasty repercussions.

smolder *SMOLE•dur* VERB

    1. to burn and smoke without flame   [The logs were damp, and the fire would only *smolder*.]

    2. to exist in a state of hidden or tightly controlled activity   [Bert's desire for revenge continued to *smolder* while he waited for his chance to get even.]

stoic *STOH•ik*

    NOUN   someone who controls his or her emotions, accepts whatever happens, and remains calm in spite of pain or suffering   [Everyone was amazed that Simone could be such a *stoic* during her illness.]

    ADJECTIVE   unemotional; calm and unbothered by suffering; self-controlled   [It was bitterly cold, but Misha walked on in *stoic* silence.]

vile *VILE* ADJECTIVE

    disgustingly bad   [That movie is so *vile* that I can't believe anyone can sit through it.]

Exercise A: What Is It?

Write the Word that each clue describes.

1. This is easy for some people to understand but hard for others. _____

2. Barbecue coals do this for a time after the flames die down. _____

3. The more of this a thing has, the harder it is to stop it. _____

4. This is one thing people get from having traditions. _____

5. Teenagers sometimes go to a mall to do this. _____

Exercise B: Rhyme Time

Write the Word that best completes each rhyme.

Daft
Poem 3

Mary's doctor
often told her
Not to let her anger
smolder. So she took
some actions bolder.
Now a prison cell
will hold her
Till she's gotten
much, much
older.

6. What is this dinner? Roasted crocodile?
   I've never tasted anything so ___! _____

7. The gymnast had such skill and flexibility
   That she did every stunt with great ___. _____

8. My sister's teeth are perfect, but not mine.
   Though, after I've had braces, they'll ___. _____

9. He laughs, he sobs, but he is still heroic.
   Who thinks today that courage must be ___? _____

10. I'd like to go to parties and arcades, but I just can't.
    I do not have the time to ___! _____

Exercise C: Antonyms

Write the Word that means the opposite of each underlined word or phrase.

11. Don't be sassy and stir up your parents even further; try to ___
    them by apologizing. _____

12. I tried to separate myself from Moe and Rena's activities because
    I didn't want to ___ myself with such troublemakers. _____

13. Come up with one sensible suggestion instead of all these ___ ones. _____

14. Gayle's reaction to the salesman was trusting, but Alicia was ___. _____

15. Anger may burst out in loud words or just ___ under the surface. _____

16. Clyde is such a crybaby; I wish he could be more of a ___. _____

17. Is soft music harmful to your concentration or ___ to it? _____

Exercise D: True or False
Circle TRUE or FALSE for each statement.

18. One who is the **epitome** of fashion may qualify for a "best dressed" award. . . . .   TRUE   FALSE

19. Getting a good job is a likely **repercussion** of dropping out of school. . . . . .   TRUE   FALSE

20. A playground's **facilities** might include swings and jungle gyms. . . . . . .   TRUE   FALSE

21. Eating only sugary foods would be **conducive** to good health. . . . .   TRUE   FALSE

22. A ringing alarm breaks the **continuity** of one's sleep. . . . .   TRUE   FALSE

23. A driver uses brakes to increase **momentum**. . . . .   TRUE   FALSE

Exercise E: Analogies
Write the letter of the word that completes the analogy.

____ 24. *cold : cool ::* **daft** *:*
   A. sick   B. silly   C. mean   D. clumsy

____ 25. *delightful :* **vile** *:: long :*
   A. dull   B. good   C. short   D. endless

____ 26. *uniform : clothing ::* **jargon** *:*
   A. belief   B. singing   C. language   D. occupation

____ 27. **mollify** *: anger :: dim :*
   A. lights   B. flames   C. tantrum   D. evening

Daft
Poem 4
Kyle ran a
Mile from a
Vile rep-
Tile.

"Me? Vile? I think I
deserve an apology."

Exercise F: Synonyms
Write the Word that could be used in place of each underlined word or phrase.
This exercise continues on the next page.

28. Please put the books on the shelf so their
spines <u>are even</u> with the edge.   _____

29. Okay, so you think my plan is <u>nuts</u>; that
doesn't mean I can't make it work.   _____

30. "Paying attention is generally <u>helpful</u> to
learning," said Ms. Green sternly.   _____

31. One <u>result</u> of the flood was that people
lost their jobs at businesses damaged by it.   _____

32. The coach's <u>doubtful</u> comment indicated
he thought my excuse was suspicious.   _____

Daft
Poem 5
"I'm sorry"
will not
qualify.
My rage it
will not
mollify.
My mood it
will not
jollify.

33. A particularly <u>gross</u> color combination is brown and lime green. _____

34. Elena's <u>skill and efficiency</u> at drawing is absolutely amazing. _____

35. That player is the <u>perfect example</u> of good sportsmanship. _____

Exercise G: Fill-in
_____

Write the Word that best completes each sentence.

36. Did people think the Wright brothers were _____ when they said they were building a flying machine?

37. A child might suffer from a lack of _____ in life if his or her family moves often.

38. I tried not to show how _____ I was, but I truly did not believe a word he said.

39. Would you _____ the edges of the cloth so that I can pin them together?

40. A campfire may _____ even after you think it's out, so be careful.

41. One must know computer _____ to make sense of "reboot," "download files," and "surf the Net."

42. Increased pollution was just one _____ of building a factory on the lake shore.

43. The ballet dancer in the starring role was the _____ of graceful strength.

44. The gym is being repainted, so we use a _____ at the local park field house.

45. The movie's villain did such _____ things that she deserved the punishment she got.

46. If I were rich, I would _____ around the world, going wherever I pleased.

47. Amanda's _____ response to the tragedy in her life made us wonder if she was made of stone.

48. The truck's _____ was so great that it broke right through the wall it hit.

49. Karen tried to _____ Woody, but nothing she did decreased his rage.

50. Working together can be _____ to friendship, and Wade and Dustin developed strong ties during the summer they were both camp counselors.

align V.
conducive ADJ.
continuity N.
daft ADJ.
epitome N.
facility N.
gallivant V.
incredulous ADJ.
jargon N.
mollify V.
momentum N.
repercussion N.
smolder V.
stoic N., ADJ.
vile ADJ.

Daft Poem 6
The melons fell down to the floor
And picked up such momentum
That when they rolled right
out the door,
Nobody could prevent 'em.

Lesson 14

abstain   *ab•STAIN*   VERB

to hold back from doing or participating in something   [If you have an upset stomach, you should *abstain* from eating spicy food.]

balderdash   *BALL•dur•dash*   NOUN

talk or writing that is worthless because it makes no sense   [Katrina thought the poem was brilliant; I thought it was *balderdash*.]

canny   *KAN•ee*   ADJECTIVE

clever and cautious; showing sharp understanding in one's dealings   [Merilee always has money because she's *canny* about spending it.]

dogged   *DOG•id*   ADJECTIVE

not giving in readily; staying with an activity in a steady way   [Paula kept working away in a *dogged* manner even after the rest of us had quit and gone home.]

enlighten   *en•LITE•un*   VERB

to provide information in a way that frees one from ignorance; to give the light of knowledge to   [A week on my uncle's ranch was enough to *enlighten* me about the difficulties of cattle ranching.]

haggard   *HAG•urd*   ADJECTIVE

having a worn look, as from grief, illness, or strain   [The photos captured the *haggard* faces of the refugees.]

humdrum   *HUM•drum*   ADJECTIVE

boringly ordinary   [I wish something exciting would interrupt my *humdrum* existence.]

oaf   *OAF*   NOUN

a clumsy, stupid person   [It's better to be an *oaf* on the dance floor than in personal relationships.]

plagiarize   *PLAY•juh•rize*   VERB

to copy written work done by someone else and present it as one's own   [If you *plagiarize* a magazine article instead of writing your own report, you won't deserve a passing grade.]

plummet   *PLUM•it*   VERB

to fall straight down; to plunge   [If a helicopter's blades stopped turning, it would *plummet* to the ground.]

savagery   *SAV•ij•ree*   NOUN

1. the condition of being wild, fierce, or untamed   [The dog, which had never had an owner, showed the *savagery* of a wolf.]

2. an act of cruelty or fierceness   [We were horrified by the *savagery* of the attack.]

tangible   *TAN•juh•bul*   ADJECTIVE

1. able to be touched or felt by touch; having physical form   [The coins in his pocket were a *tangible* reward for his work.]

2. specific enough to be grasped with the mind; definite; not vague   [The cops suspected Lefty McGurk of the burglaries, but they hadn't yet found any *tangible* proof of his guilt.]

The dishonest Lefty McGurk
Would burgle and steal with a smirk.
　　He hadn't much brain,
　　　But he couldn't abstain
　　　　From attempting unscrupulous work.

　　Well, McGurk was an oaf, and his goof
　　Was to trip and to fall through a roof.
　　　Now, it sure isn't canny
　　　To fall on your fanny
　　　　While holding a huge sack of proof.

The cops' ultimatum:
"Freeze, Lefty!"

ultimatum   *ul•tuh•MATE•um*   NOUN

a final demand—one that, if refused, will end all dealings   [The landlord gave the Smiths an *ultimatum*: "Pay up or move out."]

unscrupulous   *un•SKROO•pyuh•luss*   ADJECTIVE

without moral principals   [Jody is *unscrupulous* in getting what she wants; she'll do anything.]

zany   *ZAY•nee*   ADJECTIVE

funny in a foolish or crazy way   [*I Love Lucy* is a TV show famous for the *zany* adventures of the main character, Lucy.]

Exercise A: Questions

USE A WORD ONLY ONE TIME IN EACH EXERCISE.

Write the Word that best answers the question.

1. What must a patient do with regard to activity when a doctor orders complete bed rest?

   _____

2. What describes people who refuse to let failure stop them?

   _____

3. What would a rock do if you dropped it from a roof?

   _____

4. What do teachers attempt to do to their students?

   _____

5. What would an honest writer *never* do?

   _____

Exercise B: Antonyms

Write the Word that is an antonym for each set of words.

6. exciting; interesting; extraordinary

   _____

7. energetic; bright-eyed; rested

   _____

8. honest; fair; trustworthy

   _____

9. faint; uncertain; unclear

   _____

10. suggestion; request; plea

    _____

11. kindness; tenderness; mercy

    _____

A woman fell from a third-story window and plummeted to the ground below. A man rushing to help asked her what had happened. "I haven't a clue," she said. "I just got here myself!" ∎

"I do know this sidewalk is tangible!"

Exercise C: Synonyms

Write the Word that could be used in place of each underlined word or phrase.

12. Oh, please! That excuse is pure <u>nonsense</u>.

    _____

13. The <u>viciousness</u> of Mandy's response was shocking.

    _____

14. Brita's <u>ongoing and determined</u> efforts finally paid off.

    _____

15. To be healthier I have to <u>stop myself</u> from eating junk food.

    _____

16. I don't understand the game; please <u>educate</u> me about the rules.

    _____

17. Joel's <u>silly, comical</u> behavior gave him a reputation as class clown.

    _____

18. The splintered door frame was <u>actual</u> proof that someone had broken into the house.

    _____

19. That candidate's <u>smart, sly, knowing</u> approach to running a campaign won the election.

    _____

Exercise D: Matching

Match each phrase on the left to the phrase on the right
that means the same, or nearly the same, thing.

____ 20. observe an *oaf*   A. purposeful private eye

____ 21. *canny* customer   B. steal some sentences

____ 22. *dogged* detective   C. behold a bungler

____ 23. playfully *plummet*   D. everyday event

____ 24. *humdrum* happening   E. fall fast for fun

____ 25. *plagiarize* a paragraph   F. sharp shopper

Exercise E: Analogies

Write the letter of the word that completes the analogy.

____ 26. *cheater* : *unscrupulous* :: *genius* :
    A. foolish B. famous C. intelligent D. considerate

____ 27. *laugh* : *cry* :: *plummet* :
    A. soar   B. roll   C. crawl   D. spread

____ 28. *lion* : *savagery* :: *lamb* :
    A. wool   B. sheep   C. pasture   D. gentleness

____ 29. *give* : *take* :: *enlighten* :
    A. ignore B. change C. confuse D. burden

A giraffe, a turtle, and an elephant arrived at a small watering hole at the same time. The turtle said to the elephant, "Watch your step, you big oaf!"

The elephant picked up the turtle, tossed it high in the air, and then grinned as it plummeted into a nearby dune.

The canny giraffe moved to a safer distance before saying, "Enlighten me, please, as to why you responded with such savagery to such a mild little insult!"

"Aw, the insult was nothing," the elephant sniffed. "I recognized him as the same unscrupulous old turtle who cheated me seventeen years ago."

Exercise F: Put It Briefly

Write the Word that best completes each sentence. This exercise continues on the next page.

30. With wild animals as my enemies, cleverness and bravery weren't enough. I needed something solid—a club or another real object—that I could use as a weapon. *Briefly*, I needed something . . . . _____

31. Milton wasn't being serious, not at all. He was being nutty, and he entertained everyone with his goofy, wild, dizzy, absurd behavior. *Briefly*, Milton was being . . . . _____

32. That guy insults people without meaning to, says exactly the wrong thing at the wrong time, behaves like a numbskull and a bonehead, and is a dope. *Briefly*, he's a real . . . . _____

33. There wasn't anything reasonable in the argument. Every objection was stupid and silly, the points she made were ridiculous, and the ideas were baloney. *Briefly*, the argument was total . . . . _____

34. My boss put her foot down, saying that things were going to change and I had no choice about it. I could either do as she said, or she'd fire me. That was that. *Briefly,* she gave me a clear . . . .   _____

35. The woman looked overworked and exhausted. She had circles under her eyes; she was pale; she appeared to be ready to collapse from worry and trouble. *Briefly,* she was . . . .   _____

Quick LIST

abstain V.

balderdash N.

canny ADJ.

dogged ADJ.

enlighten V.

haggard ADJ.

humdrum ADJ.

oaf N.

plagiarize V.

plummet V.

savagery N.

tangible ADJ.

ultimatum N.

unscrupulous ADJ.

zany ADJ.

"Goodness," replied the giraffe, "seventeen years ago! You have an amazing memory!"

"Yup," the elephant said. "Turtle recall." ∎

"Usually my parachute opens."

Question:
What do you have when an unscrupulous cheater is half-buried in sand?

Answer: Not enough sand

Exercise G: Fill-in

Write the Word that best completes each sentence.

36. The _____ actions of the circus clowns made the children howl with laughter.

37. My parents _____ from drinking coffee at night because it keeps them from sleeping.

38. Mitchell is so _____ about making a bargain that he almost always comes out on top.

39. Danielle felt like a total _____ when she knocked over the shelves at the store.

40. Listen carefully while I try to _____ you, and then maybe you'll understand.

41. Grizzly bears are known for their _____, so every effort should be made to avoid them.

42. It's both lazy and dishonorable to _____ other people's work instead of doing your own.

43. A storekeeper with a reputation for being _____ will soon have few customers.

44. Both Mr. and Mrs. Rodriguez looked _____ after a week as new parents with little sleep.

45. The paper Alf handed in was a _____ indication that he has been working harder.

46. A hawk or an eagle may _____ from the sky to snatch a chicken or rabbit from the ground.

47. That rumor is just _____; surely nobody would believe such rubbish.

48. It was the _____ efforts of two FBI agents, who never gave up, that finally led to the criminal's capture.

49. I spent a _____ day, following my usual routine and wishing something interesting would happen.

50. His _____ was clear; if she didn't agree to marry him, he would break up with her.

Lesson 15

adversity ad•VUR•suh•tee NOUN

a state of misery, misfortune, or distress [Eli's family faced great *adversity* when his father lost his job and their house burned down.]

avarice AV•uh•riss NOUN

too great a desire for money or possessions [His *avarice* caused him to cheat others for his own personal gain.]

chronological kron•uh•LOJ•ih•kul ADJECTIVE

arranged in the order in which events happened [List the major battles of World War II in *chronological* order.]

embellish em•BEL•ish VERB

1. to make more attractive by adding decorations [I think I will *embellish* this coat with fancier buttons.]

2. to make more interesting by adding details, sometimes fictitious ones [Cyrus doesn't lie exactly, but he tends to *embellish* the truth.]

excruciating ex•KROO•she•ay•ting

ADJECTIVE causing extreme suffering; very painful [The medication helped relieve the *excruciating* pain.]

feasible FEE•zuh•bul ADJECTIVE

capable of being carried out; sensible and likely to be successful [Is painting the whole house this week a *feasible* plan?]

hindsight HIND•site NOUN

the ability to see, after an event, what should have been done [In *hindsight*, it's clear that we should have taken a bus instead of walking.]

"Hindsight tells me that walking over the dog was not the most feasible way to get across the hall. Maybe if I just stand here unobtrusively for a while . . ."

impede im•PEED VERB

to delay with difficulties or stand in the way of [An accident on a busy road can *impede* the flow of traffic.]

impervious im•PUR•vee•us ADJECTIVE

1. not allowing something to pass through or penetrate [The plastic is *impervious* to water.]

2. not affected or influenced by [Polar bears seem completely *impervious* to the cold.]

insolence IN•suh•lunce NOUN

extreme disrespect that is deliberately insulting or rude [The *insolence* of the clerk was so shocking to my aunt that she swore she would never shop at that store again.]

legacy LEG•uh•see NOUN

1. a gift of money or property from a person who has died [The man's grandson received a *legacy* of several thousand dollars.]

2. anything handed down from the past [Distrust and resentment between the North and South was a lasting *legacy* of the Civil War.]

plod PLOD VERB

1. to move slowly but steadily [The weary hikers had to *plod* through deep snow.]

2. to work without enthusiasm or energy [Jessica sighed as she began to *plod* through her homework assignment.]

rant RANT

VERB to speak loudly and wildly [When Dad picked up the phone bill, I knew he was going to *rant* about wasting money.]

NOUN a loud, wild speech [The man's long *rant* included the claim that beings from another planet had taken over the government.]

unobtrusive un•ub•TRU•siv ADJECTIVE

not calling attention to oneself or itself; barely noticeable [The play had begun, so I tried to slip into the auditorium in an *unobtrusive* way]

wan WAHN ADJECTIVE

1. a lack of color in the face, often due to exhaustion or illness [Corey looked quite *wan* when he had the flu.]

2. lacking energy; weak in spirit or action [Gloria responded with a *wan* smile at my efforts to cheer her up.]

Words to Go!

USE A WORD ONLY ONE TIME IN EACH EXERCISE.

Exercise A: When . . .
Write the Word that best completes each sentence.

1. When I lost my temper and carried on about how unfair everything was and how horribly I'd been treated, my speech was a . . . . _____

2. When the potato crop failed in Ireland and people had no money, no food, and little hope for the future, they suffered from great . . . . . . _____

3. When people know exactly what plays would have worked better in yesterday's football game and what decisions were mistakes, they have the benefit of . . . . _____

4. When King Midas asked for and got the power to turn everything he touched to gold, and then his food and water and even his daughter did, he soon regretted his . . . . _____

5. When you organize a photo album with your baby pictures first and then those of you at age one, age two, and so on, the arrangement you use is . . . . _____

Exercise B: Synonyms
Write the Word that could be used in place of each underlined word or phrase.

6. We decided to underline{trudge} onward for another mile, if we could. _____

7. Ana made a underline{faint and feeble} response to my suggestion. _____

8. We are trying to come up with a underline{workable} plan. _____

9. Madeline sewed shiny beads on her plain dress to underline{beautify} it. _____

10. It seems that her underline{greed} will never be satisfied. _____

11. Enrique overcame underline{hardship} to get where he is today. _____

12. Crowds on the sidewalk will underline{interfere with} a jogger's progress. _____

13. The sudden cramp in my leg was underline{unbearable}. _____

Exercise C: Yes or No
Circle YES or NO for each statement. This exercise continues on the next page.

14. Are assistants supposed to *impede* those they work for? . . . .   YES   NO

15. Can a *legacy* be something besides money or objects—such as freedom? . . . .   YES   NO

16. Are hugs and kisses supposed to be *excruciating*? . . . .   YES   NO

17. Would it be *feasible* to replace all police cars with bicycles? . . . .   YES   NO

LESSON 15   79

18. Can a person look at something in *hindsight* while it is occurring? . . . . YES   NO

19. Do roses made of frosting *embellish* a birthday cake? . . . . YES   NO

20. Do people who are excited about their jobs usually *plod* through their work? . . . . . . YES   NO

Exercise D: Opposites
Write the **Word** that best completes each sentence.

Nothing impeded Henry from practicing his violin. Day after day, he plodded through his lessons, note by note.

Unfortunately, the cat screeched and howled along with each note. To Henry this accompaniment was an amusing embellishment. To his family, it was excruciating torture.

Finally unable to stand one more screeching note, Henry's sister stormed into his room one night. "Henry, please," she pleaded, "couldn't you play something the cat doesn't know?" ■

"Does she think I like it? It's cruelty to animals!"

21. Ann struts around and likes to be the center of attention, but Jan tries to be . . . .   _____

22. Criticism really upsets Cal, but don't bother to criticize Hal because he is . . . .   _____

23. Most of Bree's ideas are pretty crazy and not likely to work, but Bea's are usually . . . . .   _____

24. Hank looks quite healthy with his rosy-pink cheeks, but Frank is . . . .   _____

25. May is humble and courteous to her elders, but Fay's behavior and attitude show . . . .   _____

26. When Mick is upset, he gets moody and silent, but Nick is likely to . . . .   _____

27. Lu's life has been full of blessings and happiness, but Sue has had to deal with . . . . .   _____

Exercise E: What Is It?
Write the **Word** that each clue describes.

28. A time line has this kind of organization.   _____

29. This describes a warning that is a little kick under the table or a slight nudge.   _____

30. A piece of jewelry passed from generation to generation would be this.   _____

31. Dull stories can be made more entertaining if the storytellers do this to them.   _____

32. This is like sassiness but even more impolite because it involves scorn.   _____

33. This involves a looking back, but not the kind that uses a rearview mirror.   _____

34. A black-out curtain is this to light; a good roof is this to rain.   _____

35. This is what night or a snowstorm could do to a search for a lost hiker.   _____

Quick LIST

adversity N.

avarice N.

chronological ADJ.

embellish V.

excruciating ADJ.

feasible ADJ.

hindsight N.

impede V.

impervious ADJ.

insolence N.

legacy N.

plod V.

rant V., N.

unobtrusive ADJ.

wan ADJ.

Exercise F: Fill-in

Write the **Word** that best completes each sentence.

36. I was tired and bored, but I managed to _____ through the job of folding the laundry.

37. An impatient customer began to _____ about how slow the service was.

38. Donna's grandmother left her a _____ of two hundred shares of stock.

39. Kiyo's life contained much _____, but her determination kept her from giving up.

40. My parents think it isn't _____ to have a large family reunion at our small apartment.

41. Rocky was fired for _____ when he replied to his boss by saying, "Get off my back, old timer."

42. Fallen rocks did _____ us but did not prevent us from getting through the canyon.

43. The _____ cramp in Nelda's side made her gasp and clench her teeth.

44. Please be as _____ as possible when you go into the classroom so you don't interrupt the lecture.

45. Ms. Wu tends to _____ her slide shows with fascinating bits of information about her travels.

46. Because the gem was _____ to scratching, we decided it must be a diamond.

47. Dad said that I was looking _____ and asked me if I felt all right.

48. Carlton drove ten miles before _____ made it clear that turning left had been a mistake.

49. Most of the scenes in the movie were _____, but a few flashbacks revealed earlier events.

50. In *A Christmas Carol*, Ebenezer Scrooge's _____ leads him to pile up a fortune and refuse to share any of it until he finally sees the error of his ways.

Very late one night, a teenaged cat tried to make an unobtrusive entry into the house. He was met by his mother, however, and, as he had expected, she began to rant. She went on and on about how fearful she had been, wondering what had impeded her baby. Had he been laid low by some awful adversity? Was he lying in excruciating pain in some dark alley beyond the help of his wan mother? Impervious to her concern, the young cat said insolently, "Mom, can't you just let me lead one of my own lives?" ■

"Yeah, in hindsight, I guess I could've phoned home."

Word Fun 3!

Crossing

"Hold still. This won't hurt a bit."

Across

2. What scoldings or warnings do
6. Garments, clothes, or duds
7. This would describe a life without hope.
8. This describes foxes and clever people.
9. What quiet, obedient people or animals are
12. People who shut others out on purpose do this to them.

Down

1. Another word for *trap*
2. What you have when you have enough but still want more, more, more!
3. How two nights without sleep would leave a person
4. What you do to things that you line up evenly
5. This describes the route of many detours.
10. It's left to someone in a will.
11. You're likely to do this if you expect something to hurt.

Digging

Find and underline the **Word** from Unit 3 that is buried in each sentence. The words to dig up are *botch, daft, distort, oaf, stoic,* and *wan.*

1. Does he feel anything? He never seems to. I can't see any sign of emotion in him.

2. You'll spoil the project if you work on it like a robot. Change your attitude. Use your brain!

3. The doctor saw a new patient who was pale and had no energy.

4. There's no point in trying to teach manners to a fool like him.

5. If you think *that* was crazy, listen to what she did afterwards!

6. Hearing you twist the meaning of what I said is torture to me.

Coping with a Dope

At a time of terrible adversity in her life, a woman was forced to give up her newborn twins for adoption. One boy went to an Egyptian family and was named Amal. The other was adopted by a Mexican couple, and they named him Juan. The woman never saw her sons again, but she received occasional letters from their new parents describing the boys' progress.

Defining

Match the invented word to its meaning.

_____ 1. *quackuisition*

_____ 2. *repercushion*

_____ 3. *ultimuttum*

_____ 4. *advarsity*

_____ 5. *splarge*

A. what a parent gives a child by saying "Feed the dog . . . or else!"

B. what the school team faces while playing a much better team

C. to please oneself by buying a bigger meal than is needed

D. a result of spending too much time on the couch

E. the purchase of a duck

Puzzling

Identify the **Word** from Unit 3 that fits the clue in each box. (The first letter is shown in the blank.) The clues in the example are the word *add* and its fancy lettering, suggesting that the **Word** is . . .

2. e _____

| Add | *Example* embellish _____ |

anti-virus, browse, cursor, hard drive, megabytes, RAM, reboot, screen saver, shut down, taskbar, window

3. j _____

| 1923 1924 1925 1926 | 1. c _____ |

"Howdy!"

4. c _____

One day, after receiving a photograph of Juan, she dolefully told her husband that she wished she had one of Amal.

"What balderdash!" the husband admonished her. "They're identical twins! If you've seen Juan, you've seen Amal!"

■

Matching

Match each phrase on the left to the phrase on the right that means the same, or nearly the same, thing.

_____ 1. impede speed

_____ 2. a vile crocodile

_____ 3. a pang in a fang

_____ 4. cope with a dope

_____ 5. extremely unseemly

A. unusually unsuitable

B. torment in a tooth

C. deal with a dunce

D. a revolting reptile

E. restrict rapidity

Lesson 16 _____

ambivalent am•BIV•uh•lunt ADJECTIVE

having conflicting feelings; uncertain due to mixed feelings [Rob was *ambivalent* about the prom; he wanted to go but hated spending the money to rent a tuxedo.]

backlog BACK•log NOUN

a collection or accumulation of tasks not done or orders not filled [Jasmine had a *backlog* of filing to do and worked late to finish it.]

cascade kass•KADE

NOUN something falling or rushing forth in great quantity, as water over steep rocks [Paolo opened his locker, and a *cascade* of books and papers poured out.]

VERB to fall as in a cascade [Catherine let her hair *cascade* over her shoulders.]

cowardice KOW•ur•diss NOUN

lack of courage [Kurt showed his *cowardice* by lying about the accident instead of taking responsibility for it.]

eerie EAR•ee ADJECTIVE

unusual or unnatural in a way that causes a vague uneasiness or fear [The strange howling that came from the house was *eerie*.]

hodgepodge HOJ•poj NOUN

a jumbled mixture of things [Our furniture doesn't really go together; it's a *hodgepodge* of items we've acquired over the years.]

impel im•PEL VERB

to cause by some kind of force, either physical or not physical [Did fear *impel* you to run from the scene?]

jubilation joo•buh•LAY•shun NOUN

great joy, usually with feelings of triumph [We expressed our *jubilation* with loud cheers.]

parody PAIR•uh•dee NOUN

an exaggerated imitation of something for the purpose of making fun of it [One scene was a *parody* of game shows in which every contestant was both annoying and unbelievably dumb.]

queasy KWEE•zee ADJECTIVE

feeling physical or emotional uneasiness; somewhat sick to one's stomach [Just the thought of riding one of those giant roller coasters makes me *queasy*.]

refrain ri•FRAIN

NOUN a phrase or verse that is repeated at the end of each section of a poem or song [The singer asked us to join in on the *refrain*.]

VERB to hold back from doing something [Please *refrain* from shouting in the library.]

saga SAH•guh NOUN

a long, detailed story, usually about legendary figures or historical events [The book was a *saga* of the South that told the story of many generations of one family.]

stupor STOO•pur NOUN

a condition in which the mind and senses are so dulled that one can barely think, act, or feel; a state of being nearly unconscious [Bonita was exhausted; she flopped down on the couch and fell into a *stupor*.]

Question:
What happened to the worm after she fell into a stupor inside Sir Lancelot's apple?

Answer: She woke up in the middle of the knight.

The day before:
"I feel queasy. Dizzy. Hope I don't fain—"

transient TRAN•shunt ADJECTIVE

passing with time; temporary [I had a sudden but *transient* feeling of anger that faded when I thought about the situation.]

tyranny TEAR•uh•nee NOUN

cruel and unjust government by a person or group having complete power; very cruel and unjust use of power or authority [Mr. Lucas's word is law in his household, and his entire family suffers under his *tyranny*.]

Exercise A: Yes or No

Circle YES or NO for each statement.

USE A **WORD** ONLY ONE
TIME IN EACH EXERCISE.

1. Would you tell a person in a *stupor* to calm down? . . . . .   YES   NO

2. Does feeling *queasy* make you want a big meal? . . . . . .   YES   NO

3. Would the use of spurs *impel* a horse to move? . . . .   YES   NO

4. Would it be usual to write *sagas* on postcards? . . . .   YES   NO

5. If a big dam broke, would a *cascade* result? . . . .   YES   NO

Question:
Why did the rooster
feel impelled to cross
the road?
chicken.
to prove he was no
Answer: He had

Exercise B: Synonyms

Write the **Word** that is a synonym for each set of words.

6. propel; drive; push   _____

7. weird; mysterious; creepy   _____

8. brief; momentary; short-lived   _____

9. rejoicing; excitement; happiness   _____

10. harshness; dictatorship; iron rule   _____

11. daze; numbness; stunned condition   _____

*"Actually, Chicken
Little told me the sky
was falling and said
I'd get a better view
from the other side."*

Exercise C: What Is It?

Write the **Word** that each clue describes.

12. When your work should be done but isn't, this is what remains.   _____

13. This copies something and mocks it at the same time.   _____

14. To accuse people of being chicken is to accuse them of this.   _____

15. To sing a song with five verses, you might sing this five times.   _____

16. The American Revolution was fought against this.   _____

17. Anything ghostly might be described with this word.   _____

18. A dinner made up of a week's worth of leftovers might be this.   _____

19. If it's here today and gone tomorrow, this describes it.   _____

20. Many people would feel this way about watching an operation.   _____

Exercise D: Antonyms

Write the Word that means the opposite of each underlined word or phrase.

Quick LIST

ambivalent ADJ.
backlog N.
cascade N., V.
cowardice N.
eerie ADJ.
hodgepodge N.
impel V.
jubilation N.
parody N.
queasy ADJ.
refrain N., V.
saga N.
stupor N.
transient ADJ.
tyranny N.

21. People's morals can ___ them to do certain things and <u>prevent</u> them from doing certain other things.

22. Jed was ___ about marriage, but his feelings became <u>sure and positive</u> soon after he met Roberta.

23. Beth's luggage is a ___ of this and that, but Allie has a <u>matched set</u>.

24. The winners were filled with ___, and the losers with <u>sorrow</u>.

25. Water used to ___ from this faucet; now it won't do any more than <u>dribble</u>.

26. Pat tried to ___ from laughing, but she finally just had to <u>let loose</u> with a howl.

27. You might expect small dogs to show ___, but they often demonstrate great <u>bravery</u>.

28. The joys of a happy childhood are ___, but their effects can be <u>permanent</u>.

29. The bumpy boat ride made me ___; now that I'm back on shore, I feel <u>fine</u>.

30. Eva's ability to tell what I was thinking was ___; it didn't seem <u>normal</u> to me.

Exercise E: Put It Briefly

Write the Word that best completes each sentence. This exercise continues on the next page.

31. I can't get my bike fixed right away. The bike shop has eighteen bikes waiting to be repaired. They've been there longer and have to be fixed before mine. *Briefly*, the bike shop has a . . . .

32. Supposedly it's a horror movie, but it doesn't even try to be scary. It's just funny. While creepy music plays, this insane guy sneaks up on people, ties them up, and gives them bad haircuts. Of course, this ruins their lives. *Briefly*, this movie is a . . . .

33. Do I like summer? Yes and no. I love sleeping late, but I hate not having things to do. I love going swimming, but I hate mowing the lawn. I love lots of things about the season and hate other things. *Briefly*, summer makes me feel . . . .

34. The TV show went on for six nights. Set in Texas and packed with adventure, it covered events from the fall of the Alamo all the way through World War I. *Briefly*, the show was a . . . . _____

35. Evelyn wasn't asleep, but she didn't seem awake. I smiled, but she didn't notice. I spoke, but she didn't respond. When I nudged her, she said, "Huh? What?" *Briefly*, Evelyn had been in a . . . . _____

Exercise F: Fill-in

Write the **Word** that best completes each sentence.

36. Fast-melting snow turned the little stream into a _____ that tumbled wildly down the mountainside.

37. My steak was so rare that it made me feel _____ to try to eat it, so I just pushed it to the side of my plate.

38. Would Americans ever put up with _____ after having known freedom and democracy?

39. Audrey experienced a sense of _____ as she realized that her long, hard efforts had been successful.

40. If Garth and Glenn could _____ from teasing each other, they would get along better.

41. Yanking the leash will _____ a dog to follow you, but gentle training can accomplish the same thing.

42. The store has a _____ of orders that must be filled as soon as the supplies come in.

43. There is a _____ of stuff in the big drawer that my grandfather calls his "junk drawer."

44. It was _____ to see what I had dreamed about actually take place the next day.

45. A _____ about Viking warriors wasn't what Mom had in mind when she asked Dad to tell us a bedtime story.

46. I'm sort of _____ about starting high school; I'm excited, but I'm also scared.

47. Charlie was in a _____ and didn't seem to know what was happening around him.

48. We teased Janelle about her _____ when she was too scared to ride a horse.

49. Happily, the bitter cold of winter is _____ and will eventually be replaced by the warmth of spring.

50. We had read a story in English class, and Cora wrote a _____ of it that was so funny even the teacher laughed out loud.

Question: How can you prevent diseases caused by biting insects?

Answer: Refrain from biting any.

Lesson 17 _____

adjacent *uh•JAY•sunt* ADJECTIVE

next to; near or close (to something) [We can park in the lot *adjacent* to the store.]

assess *uh•SESS* VERB

to examine in order to judge the quality, value, or significance of something [The insurance company will *assess* the damage to the car to figure out how much the repairs will cost.]

bemoan *bi•MOAN* VERB

to mourn over or complain about [Walking to school made Judy *bemoan* the loss of her bike.]

coexist *koh•ig•ZIST* VERB

1. to exist at the same time or place [Dinosaurs and people did not *coexist*.]

2. to live with others peacefully despite differences [After peace has been declared, the nations will have to try to *coexist*.]

debut *day•BYOO*

NOUN a first public appearance; the first appearance of anything [The band practiced long hours for its *debut*.]

VERB to make a debut [The new team mascot will *debut* at the homecoming game.]

erratic *ih•RAT•ik* or *ur•AT•ik* ADJECTIVE

not on a steady course; not regular in action or behavior; not consistent [Luisa's pitching is *erratic*; she may be very good or just terrible.]

fiasco *fee•ASS•koh* NOUN

a complete failure, often so complete as to be ridiculous [With the lead singer out sick and the sound system broken, the concert was a *fiasco*.]

leery *LEER•ee* ADJECTIVE

suspicious or doubtful; on one's guard [Roger was *leery* of the growling dog.]

naive or **naïve** *nah•EEV* ADJECTIVE

simple or childlike in attitude; innocent [You must think I'm pretty *naive* if you expect me to believe that ridiculous story.]

paternal *puh•TUR•nul* ADJECTIVE

1. related on the father's side of the family [Your father's mother is your *paternal* grandmother.]

2. of or like a father [The coach had a *paternal* attitude toward his players and was as concerned about their general well-being as he was about their performance on the field.]

MAX: Look at this. It's a portrait of my paternal great-great-great-grandparents.
MIN: Wow! They don't look a day older than you!

quirk *KWURK* NOUN

a peculiar way of acting [One of Kerri's *quirks* is to eat all of one thing on her plate before starting on another.]

raucous *RAW•kuss* ADJECTIVE

1. harsh-sounding; hoarse [I was awakened by a crow's *raucous* cry.]

2. loud and disorderly [Mr. Wong frequently complained to his landlord about the *raucous* parties next door.]

solitude *SOL•uh•tood* NOUN

a state of being alone [A cabin in the woods gave the man the *solitude* he wanted.]

subsequent *SUB•si•kwent* ADJECTIVE

coming after; following [Ginnie decided to try harder, and her *subsequent* efforts were much more successful.]

whet *WHET* VERB

1. to sharpen (a blade) [A barber giving a shave will usually first *whet* his razor.]

2. to stimulate, make eager, or intensify [Commercials and advertisements are attempts to *whet* the public's interest in a product.]

Exercise A: What Is It?

Write the Word that each clue describes.

1. Doing this to a dull knife makes it cut better.

   _____

2. If you blow up a balloon and let it go, this describes its path.

   _____

3. A man's right to see and be involved with his children is this kind.

   _____

4. Roommates who dislike each other need to find a way to do this.

   _____

5. A group of angry people all talking at once could be this.

   _____

6. An example of this would be a driving lesson
    during which you drove into a tree.

   _____

*Min joins Max at a restaurant and proudly shows
him a ring with a huge, sparkling diamond.*
MIN: I just bought this from a guy on the street!
MAX: I'd be leery of buying a ring like that without
having a jeweler assess it first. I mean, how do you
know it's a real diamond?

MIN: Well, it had better be! If
it isn't, I just got cheated out
of ten bucks!

Exercise B: Synonyms

Write the Word that could be used in place of each underlined word or phrase.

7. My little sister is so <u>mentally immature</u> that she believes
    everything she's told.

   _____

8. Ms. Kohl used a microphone to ask the <u>rowdy</u> fans to settle
    down and be quiet.

   _____

9. Car lovers are eager for the <u>presentation</u> of that long-awaited
    new model.

   _____

10. The first performance of the play was awful, but all of the <u>later</u>
    shows were good.

   _____

11. Mr. Clark has been a family friend for years and takes a <u>fatherly</u>
    interest in my brother and me.

   _____

12. Playing loud music while she does housework is a <u>peculiarity</u>
    of my mom's.

   _____

13. There's no fence between our yard and the <u>neighboring</u> yard.

   _____

14. We're studying the animals that <u>live together</u> in our region.

   _____

15. You can't <u>evaluate</u> a cat's personality while it's sleeping.

   _____

16. The weather has been <u>unpredictable</u> this spring.

   _____

Exercise C: Antonyms

Write the **Word** that is an antonym for each set of words.

Quick LIST

adjacent ADJ.
assess V.
bemoan V.
coexist V.
debut N., V.
erratic ADJ.
fiasco N.
leery ADJ.
naive ADJ.
paternal ADJ.
quirk N.
raucous ADJ.
solitude N.
subsequent ADJ.
whet V.
_____

17. prior; earlier; preceding   _____

18. decrease; lessen; deaden   _____

19. celebrate; rejoice; delight in   _____

20. confident; certain; unconcerned   _____

21. wise; sophisticated; experienced   _____

22. success; triumph; achievement   _____

23. togetherness; companionship   _____

24. musical; sweet; mellow   _____

25. distant; faraway; apart   _____

Exercise D: Other Forms of Words

Use what you know about the **Words** to choose the correct answers.

_____ 26. An example of a common school **assessment** is
A. a test.   B. a yearbook.   C. an assembly.

_____ 27. An extremely **quirky** person might be described as
A. a snob.   B. a chicken.   C. an oddball.

_____ 28. A person could show **naiveté** (nah•eev•TAY) by being too
A. trusting.   B. energetic.   C. stubborn.

_____ 29. A **paternalistic** boss believes that employees need a lot of
A. respect.   B. freedom.   C. rules and guidance.

Exercise E: Mini-Rhyme Time

Write the **Word** that best completes each rhyme. This exercise continues on the next page.

Subsequent to her visit to a jeweler, Min is bemoaning her problems.
MIN: I am so naive! People always take advantage of me. What can I do?
MAX: Give me two hundred bucks and your car keys.

30. When you want time all to yourself,
you are in the mood for ___.   _____

31. When you rate a room's untidiness,
you ___ the mess.   _____

32. A person who is sadly lonesome,
might ___ being alone.   _____

33. A salesperson's odd habit is a clerk's ___.   _____

34. If half of four movies will be shown
    tonight for the first time, two will ___.   _____

35. If you feel both tired and distrustful of
    something, you are weary and ___.   _____

Exercise F: Fill-in

Write the Word that best completes each sentence.

36. After dealing with people all day, Mrs. Chu prefers _____ in the evening.

37. We had to dribble and shoot so the coach could _____ our skills at tryouts.

38. The first book in the series was good, but the _____ ones were pretty dumb.

39. Alphabetizing the food in the cupboard is a _____ of Uncle Morrie's.

40. This house gets little sunlight because the _____ buildings are so tall.

41. The smell of food cooking is likely to _____ your appetite for dinner.

42. I hope the six fish I bought can _____ because I have only one fish tank.

43. Tom's attendance has been _____, and his grades have suffered as a result.

44. I think it's ridiculous to _____ something if you won't even try to change it.

45. The team's worst _____ was scoring a touchdown for the other team!

46. The little boy's _____ questions made us all feel protective of him.

47. Charlotte was _____ of eating the chicken salad because it looked spoiled.

48. My mom's _____ ancestors were rich, but *her* mom's family wasn't.

49. A long, _____ quarrel in the alley last night kept all of us awake.

50. The _____ of a play is called its "opening night."

Exercise G: Writing

Imagine that you're attending the glamorous **debut** of a Broadway show. As you wait to go in, you watch other people arrive. In a paragraph or two, describe this event and the other theater-goers. First, though, decide who *you* are. You could, for example, be the writer or director, a drama critic, or a regular person who bought a ticket. Use at least THREE Words in your description.

THE LOVE COLONY

OPENING TONIGHT

Outside the theater:
MAX: This play is about my paternal great-great-great-grandparents.
MIN: Really? Hey, save my seat! That guy over there is selling diamond rings for five bucks!

Lesson 18

alacrity *uh•LAK•ruh•tee* NOUN

eager and lively willingness, usually shown by quick action [When the coach asked for volunteers, Denise raised her hand with *alacrity*.]

anecdote *AN•ik•dote* NOUN

a brief, often entertaining, story [Dad told an *anecdote* about an adventure he had as a boy.]

assert *uh•SURT* VERB

to say something strongly, without doubts [I saw the accident and will *assert* that it was the blue car that ran into the red one.]

croon *KROON* VERB

to sing softly in a gentle tone [An entertainer who uses a microphone can *croon* a gentle love song and still be heard by the audience.]

deterrent *dee•TUR•unt* NOUN

something that prevents, slows, or stands in the way of some action or activity [Many people argue about whether the death penalty is a *deterrent* to crime.]

discern *di•SURN* VERB

to see and recognize, either visually or mentally [I couldn't hear his exact words, but I could *discern* the fear in his voice.]

eminent *EM•uh•nunt* ADJECTIVE

higher than others in reputation or achievement; very important in the eyes of the world [When an *eminent* expert makes a recommendation, people listen.]

erroneous *ih•ROH•nee•us* ADJECTIVE

in error; wrong [My sister made the *erroneous* assumption that she could borrow my sweater.]

factor *FAK•tur* NOUN

one part of something that contributes to a result [The candidate's ability to relate well to individual voters was clearly a *factor* in his successful campaign.]

flippant *FLIP•unt* ADJECTIVE

joking or trying to be funny about something that should be taken more seriously [Toni grew increasingly angry with Abe as he kept being *flippant* about her problem.]

gracious *GRAY•shuss* ADJECTIVE

having or showing charm, kindness, and courtesy [I felt terrible when I broke a vase at Adam's house, but his mother was *gracious* and said not to worry about it.]

heighten *HITE•un* VERB

to become or make greater in quality, intensity, or degree [Filmmakers often use scary music to *heighten* the fearful uncertainty felt by a movie's viewers.]

interminable *in•TUR•mih•nuh•bul* ADJECTIVE

never ending or seeming endless [Mom told Susan and me to stop our *interminable* arguing immediately—or else.]

muse *MYOOZ* VERB

to think in a quiet, unhurried way [It can be helpful to *muse* about a writing assignment for a while before beginning to write.]

resourceful *ri•SOURCE•ful* ADJECTIVE

having talents, skills, knowledge, and the ability to apply them [Jolene is a popular baby-sitter because people know that she is *resourceful* enough to deal with anything.]

A man rushed up to a young female clerk in the drug store. "Do you have anything to cure hiccups? They're interminable!"

The resourceful clerk responded with alacrity, slapping the man across the face.

"Hey!" he said. "I know I can't

expect all clerks to be gracious all the time, but I don't expect them to slap me ever!"

"Well, sir," she said, "you don't

have hiccups any more, do you?"

"No," the man replied, "but I imagine that my wife out in the car still does!" ∎

A man visited an eminent physician. He had a carrot in one ear, a banana in the other, and a cucumber up his nose. "Doctor," he said, "could you run some tests to discern what's wrong with me?"

"No tests are necessary," the doctor asserted. "The problem is obvious. You're not eating properly." ∎

Exercise A: Mini-Rhyme Time
Write the Word that best completes each rhyme.

1. To firmly declare that a kick caused pain is to ___ that it hurt.

2. A modern method to defeat or discourage something is a current ___.

3. Someone who can deal with tricky problems in a strong way is forceful and ___.

4. To wonder about life's mysteries while on a ship is to ___ on a cruise.

5. If you peer through the fog and can see the intersection ahead, you ___ the turn.

Exercise B: Yes or No
Circle YES or NO for each statement.

6. Would a clear explanation **heighten** understanding? .... YES NO

7. Is a flash of lightning **interminable**? .... YES NO

8. Are **anecdotes** often divided into chapters? .... YES NO

9. Would a **gracious** person try to hurt your feelings? .... YES NO

10. Are objects harder to **discern** in the dark? .... YES NO

11. Does a **flippant** person seem to take things lightly? .... YES NO

Exercise C: Synonyms
Write the Word that could be used in place of each underlined word or phrase.

12. The speaker is a young but <u>famous and respected</u> lawyer.

13. Gerard is a very <u>welcoming and pleasant</u> person.

14. Candlelight will <u>increase</u> the romantic mood.

15. People once held the <u>mistaken</u> belief that the Earth was flat.

16. Price was a major <u>element</u> in the decision I made.

17. Candace was quick to <u>insist on</u> her innocence.

18. The concert seemed <u>much too long</u> to me.

19. Alexandria is <u>capable</u> enough to handle an emergency.

On the first day of school, the teacher began the lecture he gave every new class as a deterrent to bad behavior. "If there are any loudmouths or troublemakers in this class, I want them to please stand up now."

After a silence, one girl stood up.

"Aha! Do you consider yourself a troublemaker," the teacher asked, "or a loudmouth?"

"Neither one, sir," the girl replied graciously, "I just hated to see you standing up there all by yourself." ■

Exercise D: Completion

Choose the correct answer to complete each sentence.

____ 20. One example of an **eminent** person is a
    A. thief.   B. mail carrier.   C. Supreme Court justice.

____ 21. Something one is likely to accept with **alacrity** is
    A. an insult.   B. a dessert.   C. a punishment.

____ 22. Singers are most likely to **croon**
    A. a lullaby.   B. a fight song.   C. the national anthem.

____ 23. When people **muse**, they are often said to be
    A. in hot water.   B. in the clouds.   C. in over their heads.

Exercise E: What Is It?

Write the **Word** that each clue describes.

24. This is the kind of person you'd want with you if you were stranded on a desert island. _____

25. This is something that could begin with "Let me tell you about the time I . . ." _____

26. This is what good pitching is in winning a baseball game. _____

27. This describes your answer if you add 12 and 12 and get 25. _____

28. This is what a watchdog is to burglars and what high fences are to trespassers. _____

Exercise F: Antonyms

Write the **Word** that means the opposite of each underlined word or phrase.

29. Lenny would <u>screech and shout</u> when he sang, but Benny would _____

30. Betty was <u>unknown and ignored</u> as a writer, but Lettie was _____

31. Mitch's phone calls are always <u>brief</u>, but Rich's are _____

32. Marina does her chores with <u>reluctance</u>, but Sarina does hers with _____

33. Brent's behavior was <u>rude and thoughtless</u>, but Trent was _____

34. Hattie's conclusions are usually <u>accurate</u>, but Patty's tend to be _____

35. Rex's remark was <u>solemn, sober, and thoughtful</u>, but Lex's was _____

A man worked for years to train his dog to do standup comedy. Eventually Rover could tell hilarious anecdotes about his life as a dog and heighten their humorous effect by doing great impressions of various breeds.

The resourceful trainer got Rover on a TV talent show, but when the dog came out on stage, he froze, unable to say a word. Finally, after an interminable silence, the show went on.

Backstage, the man scolded, "You blew our one shot at stardom! What happened?"

Rover replied, "I couldn't see the cue cards." ∎

"This never happened to me when I was a crooner in Vegas."

Quick LIST

alacrity N.	croon V.	erroneous ADJ.	heighten V.
anecdote N.	deterrent N.	factor N.	interminable ADJ.
assert V.	discern V.	flippant ADJ.	muse V.
	eminent ADJ.	gracious ADJ.	resourceful ADJ.

Exercise G: Fill-in

Write the Word that best completes each sentence.

36. People who have eaten at that restaurant _____, without question, that it's the best one in town.

37. _____ hosts make their guests feel comfortable and welcome.

38. Diane likes to lie on a hillside and _____ about what she'll do when she grows up.

39. Grover's _____ reply to my criticism suggested that my opinion didn't matter to him at all.

40. Having a good director is an important _____ in producing a successful play.

41. As a _____ to swimmers, state workers put up warning signs about the dangerous tides.

42. Tami reacted to my suggestion with such _____ that I knew she thought it was a good one.

43. Mom is so _____ that she whipped up a great costume for me by using things she found around the house.

44. The more boring the slide show is, the more _____ people will think it is.

45. It's easy to _____ differences between African and Asian elephants if you look at them together.

46. I'd have a good time alone, but it would _____ my enjoyment if my best friend went with me.

47. Quotations from several _____ experts added solid support to my argument.

48. Uncle Solomon kept us amused with one _____ after another about his neighbors.

49. Felipe began to _____ a lovely ballad, and the rest of us fell silent in order to hear him.

50. Eyewitnesses may sometimes make _____ statements simply because their memories are not as good as they think.

Lesson 19 _____

adroit *uh•DROIT* ADJECTIVE

showing physical or mental skill [Jeb handled the disagreement in such an *adroit* manner that both sides ended up happy.]

altruistic *al•troo•ISS•tik* ADJECTIVE

showing unselfish concern for the welfare of others [*Altruistic* students spent several weeks organizing a food collection for the hungry.]

amenable *uh•MEE•nuh•bul* or *uh•MEN•uh•bul* ADJECTIVE

ready and willing to do what is asked or suggested [Bernie was *amenable* to Pauline's plan for the evening, so off they went.]

impair *im•PAIR* VERB

to damage or lessen the quality or strength of something; to make worse [Heavy fog can *impair* one's ability to drive safely.]

lucrative *LOO•kruh•tiv* ADJECTIVE

producing wealth; very profitable [Shoes are the most *lucrative* part of the store's business.]

melodramatic *mel•oh•druh•MAT•ik* ADJECTIVE highly emotional or overly dramatic, often in a way that exaggerates a situation or reaction [Cyril moaned in such a *melodramatic* way after he stubbed his toe that we thought he was seriously hurt.]

PET SHOP CLERK: If you don't mind my asking, ma'am, why do you want to buy three large rats, two dozen cockroaches, and all these fleas?

CUSTOMER: I'm trying to be amenable to my landlord's request. I'm moving, and he asked me to leave the apartment in exactly the same condition as I found it.

"I smell a rat. If you ask me, she's just being vindictive."

charisma *kuh•RIZ•muh* NOUN

the power to attract others through one's personality [Preston isn't especially handsome or witty or athletic, but he has so much *charisma* that people just want to be with him.]

condone *kon•DOAN* VERB

to accept, forgive, or overlook something wrong [I had to end my friendship with Rosie because I couldn't *condone* her cheating.]

depict *dee•PIKT* VERB

1. to represent in an illustration, drawing, painting, sculpture, or other art form [That painting *depicts* early morning on a farm.]

2. to describe in words [*Tom Sawyer* is a novel that *depicts* life in the mid-1800s.]

dubious *DOO•bee•us* ADJECTIVE

1. feeling doubt; unsure [Shane was *dubious* about Ella's ability to perform the solo.]

2. raising doubts in a way that creates suspicion; questionable [He was a man of *dubious* honor, so I didn't believe him.]

penitence *PEN•ih•tunce* NOUN

regret or sorrow for having done wrong [Mickey expressed his *penitence* so sincerely that I quickly forgave him.]

revelry *REV•ul•ree* NOUN

loud and very lively celebrating [After its team won the championship, the whole city joined in an evening of *revelry*.]

succinct *suk•SINKT* ADJECTIVE

saying what needs to be said without unnecessary words [Keep your answer *succinct*; it should make your point clearly but be no more than one paragraph long.]

tepid *TEP•id* ADJECTIVE

neither hot nor cold [Heat up the soup; it has become *tepid*.]

vindictive *vin•DIK•tiv* ADJECTIVE

tending to want revenge; intended as revenge [It was *vindictive* of Wayne to trip Carlos after Carlos bumped into him in the hall.]

Exercise A: Synonyms

Write the Word that could be used in place
of each underlined word or phrase.

1. Most children <u>show</u> any house as a rectangle with a pointed roof.

2. I don't strongly like or dislike her; my feelings are <u>lukewarm</u>.

3. Dillon admitted what he'd done but showed no <u>regret</u>.

*"Yeah, I'm
a bit dubious
about her too—*

4. Eve's hesitation and <u>untrusting</u> look annoyed me.

5. The player's <u>expert</u> move fooled her opponent.

6. Nina's <u>charm</u> helped to make her successful.

7. Poor eating habits can <u>reduce</u> one's health.

8. She was <u>agreeable</u> to what we proposed.

9. Sounds of <u>merrymaking</u> filled the air.

10. Mrs. Tomasso gave a <u>brief</u> reply.

11. Mom won't <u>put up with</u> lying.

*Hey! Are
you say-
ing that
I stink?"*

Exercise B: Put It Briefly

Write the Word that best completes each sentence.

12. A new biography of that movie star gives numerous examples of her mean, cruel behavior. It goes into detail about how she pushed people around. It describes some of the ways she was able to force others to do what she wanted. *Briefly*, the biography tends to ___ the star as a bully.

13. Some people just have a certain something. They appeal to others. There's something about them that's fascinating and makes them hard to resist. They tend to inspire loyalty and devotion. *Briefly*, such people have ___.

14. Telegrams were once common. People who sent them were charged by the letter, so they wrote things like "Arrived safely. Made 3 sales. Home in 2 days." They didn't provide a lot of details, just the most important facts. *Briefly*, telegrams were ___.

15. With Marjorie, nothing is just sad; it's "tragic." Nothing is just good; it's "super" or "fabulous." When she has a cold, she acts like she's at death's door. She turns even a mild criticism into a big fight. *Briefly*, life with Marjorie is ___.

Exercise C: Antonyms

Write the Word that means the opposite of each underlined word or phrase.

16. With practice, my <u>clumsy</u> cooking efforts became more ___.

_____

17. How could such <u>selfish</u> parents raise such ___ children?

_____

18. It isn't fair to <u>criticize</u> my behavior and ___ hers.

_____

19. Mr. Finn left his <u>low-paying</u> job for a more ___ one.

_____

20. Are you <u>forgiving</u> or ___?

_____

_____

Quick LIST

adroit ADJ.
altruistic ADJ.
amenable ADJ.
charisma N.
condone V.
depict V.
dubious ADJ.
impair V.
lucrative ADJ.
melodramatic ADJ.
penitence N.
revelry N.
succinct ADJ.
tepid ADJ.
vindictive ADJ.

_____

Ick! LIST

cockroach ISH!
flea YUCKY!
rat UGH!

_____

"I cannot condone this list."

Exercise D: Other Forms of Words

Use what you know about the Words to choose the correct answers.

____ 21. A ***penitent*** person has feelings of
    A. guilt.   B. anger.   C. surprise.

____ 22. ***Succinctness*** is most important in
    A. letters.   B. class notes.   C. conversations.

____ 23. An ***impairment*** to walking could be caused by
    A. shoes.   B. a bicycle.   C. a broken leg.

____ 24. A ***charismatic*** person might be compared to a
    A. mule.   B. magnet.   C. machine.

Exercise E: What Is It?

Write the Word that each clue describes.

25. This should describe a baby's bath water.

26. If this describes the quality of a used car, it doesn't seem like a good buy.

27. This describes people who regularly give to charities.

28. This describes the kind of person who is always determined to get even.

29. When this describes something, it might be called "a real gold mine."

30. This could describe someone who makes everything into a big deal.

31. Most New Year's Eve parties are likely to involve this.

Exercise F: Analogies
Write the letter of the word that completes the analogy.

____ 32. *gloomy : cheerful :: **dubious** :*
    A. certain   C. mournful
    B. cowardly   D. unfriendly

____ 33. *affection : hug :: **penitence** :*
    A. yawn   C. apology
    B. shrug   D. laughter

____ 34. ***impair** : destroy :: dampen :*
    A. dry   C. moisten
    B. soak   D. strengthen

____ 35. *excited : calm :: **amenable** :*
    A. eager   C. determined
    B. reluctant   D. experienced

Exercise G: Fill-in
Write the Word that best completes each sentence.

36. Clancy drove in such a smooth and _____ way that it was a pleasure to ride with him.

37. Everyone was _____ to the idea of a picnic, so we packed some food and headed out.

38. Tina smiled in a _____ way and said, "You'll be sorry; I'll make sure of that."

39. My boss was _____ about my ability to finish the job on time, but I was positive I could.

40. Political cartoons often _____ famous leaders in ways that make them look foolish.

41. It was _____ of Devon to give half his gifts to kids who hadn't received any.

42. I feared that my dizziness would _____ my ability to walk, so I remained where I was.

43. If a leader has _____, people will follow him or her anywhere.

44. Aunt Vivian made some _____ investments, and soon she had doubled her money.

45. Don't be so _____; it's not the end of the world!

46. Art's glass of ice water soon became _____ in the sun.

47. Coaches who _____ bad sportsmanship are not doing their jobs.

48. Fireworks and dancing in the street were part of the night's _____.

49. The description was complete, but _____ enough to fit on a postcard.

50. He has shown no _____ for his crimes; in fact, he seems proud of them.

A hotel clerk is on the phone with a complaining guest.
CLERK: Sir, this is the third time you have called. You said that the hot water was tepid. You said that revelry in the next room was keeping you awake. Now you say that your room is full of bugs! Just what is eating you?
GUEST: That's what I'd like to know!

FLEA 1: He's so melodramatic. I didn't bite him. Did you?
FLEA 2: Not yet.

Lesson 20   Words You Thought You Knew

You already know how to pronounce and use these familiar words. Now learn some of their less-familiar meanings.

air

> VERB   to express publicly   [Shannon is sure to *air* her opinion on the subject.]
>
> NOUN   **1.** a manner or way of behaving that creates a mood or gives a certain impression [Bruce's *air* of superiority got on my nerves.]
>
> NOUN   **2.** atmosphere or quality   [The hotel's lobby had an *air* of old-fashioned luxury.]

answerable   ADJECTIVE

> considered to be responsible for something [Mom said I would be *answerable* for any mess she found when she got home.]

aside   NOUN

> **1.** a remark made quietly to a listener or listeners that others present are not supposed to hear   [Chet muttered, "Give us a break," in an *aside* to me when the boss started talking.]
>
> **2.** words spoken by an actor that others onstage supposedly do not hear   [From the hero's *asides*, we knew that he didn't believe what the villain was telling him.]

champion

> VERB   to fight for, support, or defend someone or something   [Those who *champion* animals' rights object to killing rabbits for their fur.]
>
> NOUN   one who fights for another or for a cause; a supporter or defender   [She was a *champion* of working women.]

contain   VERB

> to hold back; to keep within fixed limits [Christy couldn't *contain* her eagerness and hurried in ahead of the others.]

list   VERB

> to tilt to one side   [As passengers rushed to the railing to see the killer whales, the ship began to *list* dangerously.]

moving   ADJECTIVE

> affecting the emotions; causing strong feelings [Bette got a lump in her throat while watching the *moving* scene.]

novel   ADJECTIVE

> new and unusual   [Marilyn came up with a *novel* plan that just might work.]

practice

> VERB   **1.** to make a habit of; to do regularly [I need to *practice* healthy eating.]
>
> VERB   **2.** to work at a profession   [Aunt Greta *practices* medicine in Tucson.]
>
> NOUN   **1.** a usual action or custom   [I will make it a *practice* to eat more salad.]
>
> NOUN   **2.** the exercise of a profession; a business based on a particular profession   [Aunt Greta has two partners in her medical *practice*.]

reserved   ADJECTIVE

> not showing one's thoughts and feelings; self-controlled   [She isn't unfriendly, just *reserved*.]

saddle   VERB

> to weigh down with a duty or responsibility [Why would Miss Chang decide to *saddle* us with a five-page paper over spring break?]

slight

> VERB   to fail to pay proper attention or respect to; to treat as unimportant   [Don't *slight* Pedro by failing to mention his efforts on the project.]
>
> NOUN   a rude act that involves treating someone or something as not worthy of respect or consideration   [Jane's laughter at my suggestion was a *slight* that angered me.]

trying   ADJECTIVE

> hard to bear due to strain on one's patience [Mom was exhausted after a *trying* day of waiting on grumpy people at the store.]

utter   ADJECTIVE

> complete; total   [Don't pay any attention to such *utter* nonsense.]

will   NOUN

> **1.** the mental power to make decisions and act; determination   [He has a *will* to succeed.]
>
> **2.** desire, purpose, or choice   [The people were subject to the queen's *will*.]

Exercise A: Put It Briefly
Write the Word that best completes each sentence.

1. Romeo overhears Juliet talking on the balcony and says, "Shall I hear more?" Juliet doesn't hear him, but the audience does, so they know what he's thinking. *Briefly*, what Romeo says is an ___.

   _____

2. Marlon's costume wasn't ordinary. No one else had one like it or had ever seen one like it. It was quite fresh, different, and extraordinary. *Briefly*, Marlon's costume was ___.

   _____

3. When Tyrone, our boss, wants something done, it gets done. His ideas, wishes, and intentions are all that matter. We workers have nothing to say about it. *Briefly*, we're controlled by Tyrone's ___.

   _____

4. The environment was elegant and dignified. Its chandelier, marble floor, and old paintings established a feeling or mood. They gave it a certain tone. *Briefly*, it had an ___ of formality.

   _____

5. It's hard to get to know Melanie. She rarely expresses her ideas and beliefs, and she keeps herself at a distance from other people . . . emotionally, that is. *Briefly*, she's ___.

   _____

6. The woman's story upset us, and we wanted to help her. No one could have heard it without reacting. *Briefly*, the story was ___.

   _____

Question:
Why did the ordinarily reserved cowboy have trouble containing his tears at the last roundup?

Answer:
It was such a mooving experience.

"It was just a lot of bull if you ask me!"

Exercise B: Antonyms
Write the Word that means the opposite of each underlined word or phrase.

7. Milking cows was a <u>common</u> experience for me, but it was a ___ one for Lena.

   _____

8. You shouldn't <u>avoid</u> regular tooth-brushing; you should ___ it.

   _____

9. In order to <u>relieve</u> Vinnie of his responsibility, I had to ___ myself with it.

   _____

10. Now and then Peg would awaken and <u>straighten up</u>, then doze off again and begin to ___.

    _____

11. Gary was a determined <u>enemy</u> of daylight savings time, Wendell was a ___ of it.

    _____

12. Patrick is <u>not to blame</u> for what happened, but Alec is old enough to be ___.

    _____

13. Arlene wasn't worried about <u>partial</u> failure; what she feared was ___ failure!

    _____

14. Everyone hoped for a <u>relaxing</u> weekend after the ___ week they'd had.

    _____

Exercise C: Yes or No

Circle YES or NO for each statement.

15. If it is a **practice** of yours to get up early, do you usually sleep late? . . . . . .   YES   NO

16. Is a **reserved** person likely to be described as openly affectionate? . . . .   YES   NO

17. Might someone "count to ten" to try to **contain** his or her anger? . . . .   YES   NO

18. Is a lawyer **answerable** for a crime his or her client committed? . . . .   YES   NO

19. If someone **slights** you, are you likely to feel insulted? . . . .   YES   NO

20. Could you **air** your views by discussing them? . . . .   YES   NO

21. Does a bully **champion** his or her victim? . . . .   YES   NO

Exercise D: Mini-Rhyme Time

Write the Word that best completes each rhyme.

22. The maid of honor's whispered "You can still back out!" was an ___ to the bride.

_____

23. If you're sick of your brother's inability to tell the truth, you find his lying ___.

_____

24. A woman who sighs, frowns, and wrings her hands has an ___ of despair.

_____

25. Treating Sir Lancelot as if he were "just some guy" would be a ___ to a knight.

_____

Exercise E: Synonyms

Write the Word that could be used in place of each underlined word or phrase. This exercise continues on the next page.

26. Watch out! The flagpole is beginning to tip!

_____

27. My neighbor works for a dental office downtown.

_____

28. How could Boris have acted like such an absolute fool?

_____

29. Don's incredible strength of purpose won't let him give up.

_____

30. If Lulu buys that car, she will burden herself with a huge debt.

_____

31. Charlene came up with a really original design for a doghouse.

_____

32. The last scene of the film was so sad that tears came to my eyes.

_____

33. Did you mean to disregard Walt by not inviting him to the reunion?

_____

Question: What do you call a cow that lists?

Answer: Lean beef

Question: What do you call a cow that can't give any milk?

Answer: An udder failure

34. Dealing with a stubborn child can be a <u>difficult, irritating</u> experience. _____

35. Firefighters tried to <u>stop the spread of</u> the fire so it wouldn't destroy
the whole forest. _____

Exercise F: Fill-in

Write the **Word** that best completes each sentence.

36. Juan plans to _____ architecture, so he's going
to a college that teaches the skills he'll need.

37. Jessie was in such _____ misery that it seemed as if
she'd never smile again.

38. Randal will think it's a _____ if you give him the worst seat
at the table; he's so easily insulted.

39. Due to the strength of Marcy's _____, no one can stop her once
she's made up her mind.

40. I respect Emilio's determination to _____ his favorite causes, but
he can't talk about anything else!

41. Recordings of Dr. Martin Luther King, Jr.'s _____ speech, "I Have
a Dream," can still inspire listeners today.

42. The man paced to and fro, scratching his head with an _____ of
complete confusion.

43. Dad saw my lips move and realized I had muttered a quick _____
to Lyle, so he asked what I'd said.

44. The hotel let us have our dog in our room but said we'd be _____
for any damage it did.

45. Angela isn't as cold-hearted as you might think; she's just _____.

46. Thick crowds and long lines turned shopping into a _____ event.

47. We piled sandbags along the river to try to _____ the flood.

48. Harvey had no right to quit and _____ you with his work.

49. The barn began to _____ as a result of termite damage.

50. It was a _____ design for a chair, unlike any I'd seen.

Question: How long
should veterinarians
practice medicine?

Answer: Until
they get it right!

*"Meanwhile, vets
should practice on
each other!"*

Quick LIST

air V., N.	**champion** V., N.	**moving** ADJ.	**reserved** ADJ.	**trying** ADJ.
answerable ADJ.	**contain** V.	**novel** ADJ.	**saddle** V.	**utter** ADJ.
aside N.	**list** V.	**practice** V., N.	**slight** V., N.	**will** N.

Word Fun 4!

Boxing

Fill in each set of blanks with a word you know that matches the clue. The boxed letters will spell out the answer to the question at the bottom.

1. The day subsequent to Saturday . . . .

2. What there's too much of when a party is raucous . . . .

3. Something a teacher often uses to assess students' knowledge . . . .

4. A color associated with cowardice . . . .

5. What you must do when alacrity is called for . . . .

6. What you are when you show penitence . . . .

7. Something that's interminable will never reach this . . . .

8. Having this on a diary is a deterrent to snooping . . . .

9. What kind of performance a debut is . . . .

Question: What did the tailor say when his customer fired him?   **Answer:**

Naming

Match each name to the description it goes best with.

____ 1. Mel O. Dramatuk   A. She's very important and tops in her field.

____ 2. Anne Nekdote   B. He makes a big deal out of everything.

____ 3. Luke Rahtiv   C. This guy's in a daze. Hey! Listen up!

____ 4. Emma Nint   D. Everything he touches turns to gold.

____ 5. Sol Littood   E. She's got a story for every occasion.

____ 6. Al Truistik   F. What a generous, giving fellow!

____ 7. Cass Kade   G. He's definitely the fatherly type.

____ 8. Bea Mone   H. Her tears flow like a waterfall.

____ 9. Pa Turnal   I. He just wants to be left alone.

____ 10. Stu Purr   J. She sure complains a lot!

A group of friends decide to see the debut showing of the new movie *Farm Wars, Part VI.*

Solving Problems

You think you have problems? Imagine being a newspaper advice columnist and trying to help these letter-writers!

I have an "eerie" problem. I want to make a novel candle for my mother-in-law. Is ear wax real wax? If I could collect enough of it, would it make a good candle? Can you think of any way I could collect my mother-in-law's ear wax without her knowing it? I'm a resourceful person, but this has me stumped.

—R.W., Eerie, Illinois

A 150-pound person is sleeping under an electric blanket that's set to 70 degrees in a room that's 55 degrees. How many calories does the person burn? If the blanket is turned off, is there any discernible difference in the number of calories, all other factors being equal?

—B.B., Zero, Alaska

I've invented a simple device that works as a deterrent to accidental injury and death. This fact alone should make it a lucrative deal for any manufacturer, but they say I need to do market research. So where can I get statistics on how many people are killed annually subsequent to being hit by falling coconuts?

—A.T., Quirk, Colorado

A-maze-ing

As a maze, this puzzle is not too amazing, but you do have to know the **Words** in Unit 4. It will also help to know them backwards and forwards!

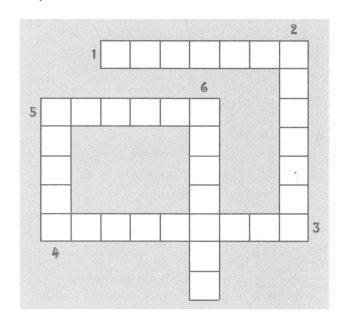

1 *Right*   Not consistent or constant; irregular

2 *Down*   What roommates and neighbors must do

3 *Left*   Not lasting or staying in one place

4 *Up*   What room temperature water is

5 *Right*   To show, describe, picture, or represent

6 *Down*   What American colonists rebelled against

Defining

Match the meaning to the invented word.

_____ 1. What a cat with deep thoughts does   A. *hambivalent*

_____ 2. A long, continuing story about a flood   B. *charismama*

_____ 3. What a tear-jerker movie about cows is   C. *mooving*

_____ 4. What an amazingly charming mother has   D. *mewse*

_____ 5. How a pig feels when it has mixed emotions   E. *sogga*

After the movie:
"It made me cry."
"I loved it. I hated it."
"I have to think about it."

Lesson 21

aboveboard *uh•BUV•bord* ADJECTIVE

honest and open; not trying to conceal anything [Kim was *aboveboard* in confessing to her part in the mischief.]

aggression *uh•GRESH•un* NOUN

1. an attack, either physical or verbal [Most people will try to defend themselves against acts of *aggression*.]

2. the quality of being hostile or threatening [A dog's growling is a sign of *aggression*.]

avert *uh•VURT* VERB

1. to turn away from something [The accident was bad, so you may want to *avert* your eyes.]

2. to prevent; to keep from occurring [To *avert* an explosion, someone had better help Sebastian with his chemistry experiment.]

burly *BUR•lee* ADJECTIVE

having a strong, sturdy build; husky [The coach was glad to see several *burly* newcomers trying out for the football team.]

chafe *CHAFE* VERB

1. to rub something in a way that causes it to become sore, worn, or irritated [Joan's leather watchband began to *chafe* her wrist.]

2. to feel or become irritated or impatient [Whenever we're planning a trip, Berta always *chafes* to get going.]

dexterity *dek•STAIR•uh•tee* NOUN

skill with one's hands or body [Leonard juggles with great *dexterity*.]

disgruntled *dis•GRUNT•uld* ADJECTIVE

discontented in an irritated, cross way; in a bad mood [Maxine was *disgruntled* about having to spend the day taking care of her little sister instead of going out with her friends.]

fluctuate *FLUK•choo•ate* VERB

to change frequently; to shift back and forth or rise and fall continuously [Don't count on its being warm on Saturday; the weather *fluctuates* at this time of year.]

heart-rending *HART•ren•ding* ADJECTIVE

deeply upsetting; heartbreaking [I read a *heart-rending* story about a lost child.]

inane *in•ANE* ADJECTIVE

lacking sense; silly [Eileen read the kids an *inane* story about a woman who lived in a shoe.]

indecisive *in•di•SY•siv* ADJECTIVE

1. unable to make a decision within a reasonable time; hesitant about making a decision [Graham was so *indecisive* about what to order that I thought we'd never eat.]

2. not deciding or settling anything [The first race was *indecisive*; it looked like a tie, so we had to run again.]

pertinent *PUR•ti•nunt* ADJECTIVE

clearly connected or related to what is going on, being discussed, or dealt with [Please ask only questions that are *pertinent* to the topic of the lecture.]

revitalize *ree•VITE•ul•ize* VERB

to give new life or energy to; to make lively or energetic again [The new gymnasium could *revitalize* the school's basketball program.]

scant *SKANT* ADJECTIVE

not enough or barely enough [We have only a *scant* supply of water; use it carefully]

uncouth *un•KOOTH* ADJECTIVE

crude; not well-mannered [My parents asked me not to embarrass them by doing anything *uncouth* when Mom's boss comes for dinner.]

A dining room
GUEST: Your dog keeps growling at me. Should I take that as a sign of aggression?
HOST'S SON: Oh, no, he's just disgruntled because you're eating off his favorite plate.

"Grrrr. It's so uncouth to eat from someone else's plate!"

Exercise A: Put It Briefly

Write the Word that best completes each sentence.

USE A WORD ONLY ONE TIME IN EACH EXERCISE.

1. The guitarist moved the fingers of one hand very precisely along the instrument's neck while her other hand picked individual strings rapidly and without error. *Briefly*, her fingers had great . . . .

   _____

2. Every detail in my report had to do with the subject, supported my point, and was appropriate. *Briefly*, the details were . . . .

   _____

3. With his muscular chest, broad shoulders, and mighty arms and legs, Travis could lift a cow and carry it to town! *Briefly*, he is . . . .

   _____

4. People trust Scott because he's genuine and frank; he doesn't lie, play tricks, or mislead anyone. *Briefly*, Scott's behavior is . . . .

   _____

5. Sometimes I like my neighbor, sometimes I don't; sometimes I enjoy being with her, sometimes I don't. *Briefly*, my feelings for her . . . .

   _____

Exercise B: Synonyms

Write the Word that could be used in place of each underlined word or phrase.

6. Gus's remark showed how <u>grouchy</u> the situation had made him.

   _____

7. The results were <u>unclear</u>, so additional testing was required.

   _____

8. My <u>small and inadequate</u> income made it hard to survive.

   _____

9. Getting stuck in a traffic jam makes me <u>fret restlessly</u>.

   _____

10. We all ignored Meg's <u>empty-headed</u> suggestions.

    _____

11. Teresa said that I was <u>gross and uncivilized</u>!

    _____

Exercise C: Matching

Match each phrase on the left to the phrase on the right that means the same, or nearly the same, thing.

_____ 12. a ***burly*** bird

_____ 13. really ***revitalize***

_____ 14. ***inane*** instructions

_____ 15. a ***heart-rending*** history

_____ 16. unquestionably ***uncouth***

_____ 17. a ***disgruntled*** descendant

A. significantly strengthen

B. a painfully pitiful past

C. a chunky chickadee

D. a grumpy grandson

E. dopey directions

F. very vulgar

A courtroom

JUDGE: You are accused of failing to avert an accident. Your car struck a comedian and dragged him eight blocks.

DRIVER: Well, actually, your honor, it was only seven blocks.

JUDGE: Whether it was seven blocks or eight is not pertinent. It is still carrying a joke too far!

Exercise D: Antonyms

Write the Word that is an antonym for each set of words.

18. thin; weak; skinny _____

19. sneaky; scheming; sly _____

20. bring on; cause; promote _____

21. contented; pleased; satisfied _____

22. brotherhood; friendship; peace _____

23. plentiful; abundant; overflowing _____

24. clumsiness; awkwardness; inability _____

Exercise E: Questions

Write the Word that best answers the question.

25. What would a tight collar do to a dog's neck? _____

26. What kind of facts should you include when you write a history report? _____

27. What might you do to your head so someone can't see your expression? _____

28. What describes people who always have trouble making up their minds? _____

29. What might building a new factory do for the economy of a dying town? _____

30. What does school enrollment do when it goes up and down from year to year? _____

31. What would describe a play or movie that made you break down in tears? _____

Exercise F: Other Forms of Words

Use what you know about the Words to choose the correct answers. This exercise continues on the next page.

_____ 32. Something that you have an **aversion** to is something you
    A. seek.   B. need.   C. avoid.

_____ 33. People who are **scantly** fed for a long time probably feel
    A. stuffed.   B. hungry.   C. content.

A doctor's office

PATIENT: Doc, it's been three months with scant improvement. I don't feel revitalized at all.

DOCTOR: Hmm. Did you follow the instructions on the medicine bottle?

PATIENT: Certainly! It said "Keep tightly closed," and I did!

DOCTOR: *Did it say "Keep brain closed"?*

Quick LIST

aboveboard ADJ.
aggression N.
avert V.
burly ADJ.
chafe V.
dexterity N.
disgruntled ADJ.
fluctuate V.
heart-rending ADJ.
inane ADJ.
indecisive ADJ.
pertinent ADJ.
revitalize V.
scant ADJ.
uncouth ADJ.

A skating rink

SKATER 1: It's nice that no one laughed when that burly fellow fell down.

SKATER 2: Yes, but the ice did make a few cracks.

____ 34. One type of person who is likely to behave **aggressively** is
   A. a bully.   B. a crybaby.   C. the class clown.

____ 35. Someone experiencing **indecision** would be most likely to say
   A. "No!"   B. "Yes!"   C. "Um, uh . . ."

Exercise G: Fill-in

Write the **Word** that best completes each sentence.

36. Robert's _____ actions shocked and offended his hosts, who will never invite him again.

37. Amy feels _____ about whether to try out for soccer because she isn't sure she'd enjoy it.

38. If your shoes _____ your feet, you're more than likely to get some nasty blisters.

39. Nell found such _____ information about her research subject that she had to choose a new one.

40. The city hopes to _____ its downtown by encouraging new stores and restaurants to open.

41. The salesperson was quite _____ in telling us about possible problems we might have with the car.

42. An expert tightrope walker has _____ as well as strength and a good sense of balance.

43. Only by steering onto the shoulder were we able to _____ a terrible collision with a stalled car on the road.

44. Uncle Cliff has been working out, and now he's too _____ to fit in his old clothes.

45. After driving thirty miles just to eat there, we were _____ when we found out the restaurant had closed.

46. Mike felt his eyes fill with tears as he listened to the _____ news report of the disaster.

47. The prices of lobster and shrimp at our local market _____ depending on how many of them the fishing boats bring in.

48. How much the dress cost was _____ to my decision about buying it, so I asked the clerk.

49. Rabbits display little _____, preferring to try to escape than to stand and fight.

50. Marta's _____ ideas have given her a reputation as quite a goofball.

A shopping mall

Home store
CUSTOMER: I don't have the dexterity to put this wallpaper on myself.
CLERK: I think it would be easier if you put it on the wall.

Restaurant
CUSTOMER: This coffee tastes like mud!
WAITER: Well, ma'am, we were quite aboveboard in describing it. The menu said it was ground this morning.

Electronics store
CLERK: Are you interested in a color TV?
CUSTOMER: Yes, but I'm indecisive about what color to get.

A classroom
TEACHER: Are you so uncouth that you think you can sleep in class?
STUDENT: Well, I could if you didn't talk so loud!

Lesson 22

accentuate *ak•SEN•choo•ate* VERB

   1. to make more noticeable; to call special attention to [Wearing these glasses will *accentuate* the shape of your face.]

   2. to stress [If a word has more than one syllable, you have to *accentuate* the right one in order to pronounce the word correctly.]

conscientious *kon•she•EN•shuss* ADJECTIVE

   careful and responsible [No matter how tired Trisha might be, she's always *conscientious* about getting to her job on time.]

expedite *EX•puh•dite* VERB

   to make easier or speed up the progress or action of [We could *expedite* the cleanup by getting more people to help.]

indulgent *in•DULL•junt* ADJECTIVE

   tending to give in to the wishes of another; kind or too kind; not strict [With an *indulgent* smile, Dad said I could skip my chores.]

invigorate *in•VIG•ur•ate* VERB

   to make lively, energetic, or full of life [A hot shower in the morning *invigorates* me.]

larceny *LAR•suh•nee* NOUN

   theft; stealing [Sofia claimed she had borrowed the car, but the police called it *larceny* because the owners hadn't given their permission.]

JUDGE: You have been charged with larceny. What do you have to say for yourself?

   DEFENDANT: I'm not guilty, sir. I'm a locksmith.

   JUDGE: Well, why were you at the store at 3:00 A.M.?

   DEFENDANT: I'm a very conscientious locksmith.

JUDGE: And why did you run when the police came?

DEFENDANT: I was just making a bolt for the door.

JUDGE: Hmm. I find you guilty; however, as this is your first offense, I'll be indulgent and give you a choice: five thousand dollars or six months in jail.

DEFENDANT: I'll take the money!

morose *muh•ROCE* ADJECTIVE

   gloomy in a bad-tempered way [Gillian was *morose* after losing the chess tournament.]

optimum *OP•tuh•mum*

   ADJECTIVE best or most favorable possible [I want to get plenty of rest to be in *optimum* condition for the game tomorrow.]

   NOUN the condition that is the best or most favorable possible [This hotel offers the *optimum* in comfort and security.]

popularize *POP•yoo•luh•rize* VERB

   to make widely known or used; to make popular [If a famous athlete shaves his head, he may *popularize* the bald look.]

pseudonym *SOO•duh•nim* NOUN

   a name used by an author instead of his or her real name [Samuel Langhorne Clemens is better known by his *pseudonym*, Mark Twain.]

reverie *REV•ur•ee* NOUN

   a daydream or the state of being unaware of one's surroundings during a daydream [Bruno was lost in a *reverie* and didn't hear anything that had been said.]

rubble *RUB•ul* NOUN

   broken bits and pieces left after something has been destroyed [After the tornado, people searched through the *rubble* of what had once been their homes.]

scandalous *SKAN•duh•luss* ADJECTIVE

   shockingly offensive or disgraceful [Some things that were considered *scandalous* in the 1800s are thought of as acceptable today.]

slapdash *SLAP•dash* ADJECTIVE

   carelessly and hurriedly done [Dora put the scrapbook together in such a *slapdash* way that some of the pages ended up glued together.]

unruffled *un•RUFF•uld* ADJECTIVE

   not even slightly disturbed; calm and unbothered [Mom remained *unruffled* even when extra people showed up for dinner.]

Exercise A: What Is It?

Write the **Word** that each clue describes.

USE A **WORD** ONLY ONE
TIME IN EACH EXERCISE.

1. Today's bathing suits would have been considered this in 1910.

2. If this describes your project for the school science fair, you'll get a low grade for effort.

3. In the saying "Many hands make light the work," this is what "make light" means.

4. An ad may do this to a particular phrase to the point that it seems everyone is saying it.

5. A person is not born with this but may become known by it.

6. To get Felix out of this, you might say, "Earth to Felix!"

7. Using a sledgehammer can turn a sidewalk into this.

8. Robbery and burglary are two types of this.

Exercise B: Synonyms

Write the **Word** that could be used in place of each underlined word or phrase.

Question:
When is fishing *not* the optimum way to relax?

Answer:
When you are the worm.

"It sure gets me ruffled."

9. What could have made Jeff so <u>glum</u> today?

10. The writer H. H. Munro used the <u>pen name</u> "Saki."

11. A good night's sleep can <u>refresh and strengthen</u> you.

12. June is <u>thorough and dependable</u> about doing homework.

13. Lola used eye shadow and mascara to <u>emphasize</u> her eyes.

14. The bike repair was so <u>sloppy</u> that a tire fell off two days later.

15. He was <u>untroubled</u> even though everything around him seemed to be going wrong.

16. This car's performance will be at its <u>maximum</u> when you use the most expensive gas.

17. Frequent bombing raids reduced large areas of the city to little more than great piles of <u>ruins</u>.

18. Marisa's <u>permissive</u> parents let her do things that my folks would never allow.

19. Everyone in town was speechless upon hearing about the mayor's <u>shameful</u> behavior.

Exercise C: Rhyme Time
Write the **Word** that best completes each rhyme.

20. All afternoon, the children shrieked and scuffled.
    But, knowing they were safe, I was ___.

    _____

21. Put "rush" on that order. Use red ink to write it.
    It's very important that they ___ it.

    _____

22. Leo cleaned the hall and stacked the benches.
    As usual, his work was ___.

    _____

23. Alarms go off. The winds mean trouble.
    This beach resort may soon be ___.

    _____

24. I'm not in total misery, but close.
    I guess I'd have to say I feel ___.

    _____

Exercise D: Antonyms
Write the **Word** that is an antonym for each set of words.

25. admirable; respectable; honorable

    _____

26. cheerful; happy; good-natured

    _____

27. panicky; upset; dismayed

    _____

28. delay; obstruct; block

    _____

29. worst; least; minimum

    _____

30. demanding; firm; harsh

    _____

Exercise E: Completion
Choose the correct answer to complete each sentence.

____ 31. Something that *invigorates* you makes you feel
         A. peppy.   B. bored.   C. embarrassed.

____ 32. To *accentuate* certain words in a letter, the writer might
         A. erase them.   B. underline them.   C. abbreviate them.

____ 33. During a *reverie*, a person makes use of his or her
         A. money.   B. imagination.   C. athletic skills.

____ 34. One person who makes a living through *larceny* is a
         A. pirate.   B. comedian.   C. tax collector.

____ 35. To greatly *popularize* a certain style would make it become
         A. a fad.   B. a danger.   C. expensive.

SON: If you give me twenty bucks, I promise that I'll be conscientious.

DAD: Oh, come on! When I was your age, I was good for nothing!

_____

Quick LIST

accentuate V.
conscientious ADJ.
expedite V.
indulgent ADJ.
invigorate V.
larceny N.
morose ADJ.
optimum ADJ., N.
popularize V.
pseudonym N.
reverie N.
rubble N.
scandalous ADJ.
slapdash ADJ.
unruffled ADJ.

Exercise F: Fill-in

Write the **Word** that best completes each sentence.

36. Clint tried to _____ the positive parts of his reaction to Emma's performance so she wouldn't be discouraged.

37. Dennis looked _____, but I think he was more disturbed about the situation than he appeared to be.

38. The painter did a _____ job, dribbling paint all over the floor and missing whole sections of the wall.

39. Mrs. Devine is a _____ teacher who works hard and won't give up on students.

40. Fresh air seems to _____ me; it makes me feel I could run for miles.

41. Anastasia looked so _____ that I wondered what bad news she had received.

42. She was an expert in _____, supporting herself for years with the sale of other people's jewelry.

43. I was wrapped up in my _____ and didn't realize that the bus had gone past my stop.

44. After the explosion, only _____ was left to show that a building had once been there.

45. The Millers have been so _____ that their children have become very spoiled.

46. Laura Lee Hope is actually the _____ of several different authors of the Nancy Drew series of mysteries.

47. The use of zip codes was begun to _____ the delivery of mail, and they were successful in accomplishing that.

48. That band's use of the accordion may _____ an instrument that musicians have neglected for decades.

49. I wanted to take my photographs under _____ lighting conditions so that every detail of the scene would show up.

50. Warren G. Harding was president during a _____ event called the Teapot Dome Affair, and it badly damaged his reputation.

Exercise G: Writing

You're writing what is sure to be a best-seller, but you plan to publish it under a **pseudonym**. On your own paper, tell what name you'd use. (Don't pick the name of a real author.) Then, in a paragraph using TWO or more **Words**, explain why you chose this particular name and why you *didn't* use your real name. Start by deciding what your book is about. This is just for fun, so use your imagination.

Three Popular Self-Help Books by Authors Using Pseudonyms

Out of the Rubble: How to Accentuate the Positive When Your Life Is a Total Mess by Sally Sunshine

Secrets of Larceny by Jay L. Byrd

Good Person! Dogg's Guide to Training People to Be Conscientious and Indulgent by Fido A. Dogg

Lesson 23 _____

arduous *AR•joo•us* ADJECTIVE
difficult to do; requiring much energy and labor [Mowing our lawn is an *arduous* task.]

aura *OH•ruh* NOUN
a certain quality that seems to come from or surround a person or thing [She had an *aura* of warmth that made me trust her.]

benign *bi•NINE* ADJECTIVE
1. kindly, gentle, and good-natured [Jude reacted to my apology with a *benign* smile.]
2. not harmful [Some tumors are signs of cancer, but some are *benign*.]

deteriorate *dee•TEER•ee•uh•rate* VERB
to make or become worse or lower in quality or value [If my cousin's health continues to *deteriorate*, she'll have to go to the hospital.]

fleeting *FLEET•ing* ADJECTIVE
lasting or remaining for only a very short time [Mr. Garrison caught just a *fleeting* glimpse of the car, so all he could tell the police was that it was green.]

humanitarian *hyoo•man•uh•TAIR•ee•un*
NOUN a person who spends a great deal of time and effort on improving the welfare of others [Albert Schweitzer, a famous *humanitarian*, ran a medical clinic in Africa.]
ADJECTIVE helping humanity [The Red Cross is a *humanitarian* organization.]

insatiable *in•SAY•shuh•bul* ADJECTIVE
too large, too strong, or too much to be satisfied [Callie's curiosity is *insatiable*; she just won't stop asking questions.]

paraphrase *PAIR•uh•fraze*
VERB to say the same thing but in different words [I don't remember Robin's exact words, but I can *paraphrase* what she said.]
NOUN a restatement using different words but containing the same idea or ideas ["To go on living or not" is a *paraphrase* of Hamlet's famous line, "To be or not to be."]

sheer *SHEER* ADJECTIVE
1. pure and unmixed [Spending the day at the amusement park was *sheer* delight.]
2. very thin and easy to see through [Sunlight comes in through our *sheer* curtains.]
3. straight up and down [Quint knew he wouldn't be able to climb the *sheer* face of the rock without using special equipment.]

spiral *SPY•rul*
ADJECTIVE circling around a central point in a flat or rising curve [Running down the *spiral* staircase made me feel a little dizzy.]
NOUN a flat or rising curve that circles or coils around a center [Some notebooks are held together by a *spiral* made of wire.]

SPIRALS spring up all over.

suffice *suh•FICE* VERB
to be enough [Will one sandwich per guest *suffice* if we also serve salad and potato chips?]

vengeful *VENJ•ful* ADJECTIVE
wanting to get even; seeking revenge [Whatever you do, don't insult Norma; she can be really *vengeful*.]

wily *WY•lee* ADJECTIVE
clever in a sneaky and tricky way [Foxes have a reputation for being *wily*.]

windfall *WIND•fall* NOUN
an unexpected profit, benefit, or gain [The twenty-dollar bill that I retrieved from the gutter was a *windfall*.]

zealous *ZEL•us* ADJECTIVE
having a strong, enthusiastic interest in something; intensely dedicated [Hayley is a *zealous* jogger who runs no matter what the weather is or what else she needs to get done.]

Words to Go!

Exercise A: When . . .
Write the Word that best completes each sentence.

USE A WORD ONLY ONE
TIME IN EACH EXERCISE.

1. When you make a pot by taking a long rope of clay, forming a circle with part of it, and then winding the clay around on itself, higher and higher, the shape of the rope of clay is a . . . . _____

2. When Donald hurts Ronald, and Ronald hurts Donald in return, and then Donald gets back at Ronald, so Ronald is determined to get back at Donald, both Donald and Ronald are being . . . . _____

3. When you can't quote someone exactly, but you can provide the same basic meaning in what you do say, what you say is a . . . . _____

4. When a person spends time and energy in efforts to relieve suffering or feed the hungry or help the helpless, that person is a . . . . _____

5. When you get something good that you hadn't looked forward to getting because you had no idea you would, what you get is a . . . . . . _____

Exercise B: Synonyms
Write the Word that could be used in place of each underlined word or phrase.

6. Plowing a field or garden can be <u>difficult and exhausting</u>. _____

7. Roberto is <u>unable to get enough</u> when it comes to ice cream. _____

8. I can't believe the <u>complete and total</u> stupidity of that remark! _____

9. She is <u>very eager and intense</u> in her efforts to get children to read. _____

10. There was quiet for a <u>brief</u> moment before the shouting began again. _____

11. According to the weather forecast, a winter coat won't be needed today; a sweater or light jacket will <u>do</u>. _____

12. In many folktales, a small, weak animal gets the best of a bigger, stronger one by being <u>sly</u>. _____

13. The dirty floor, mud-colored walls, and cracked plastic chairs gave the room an <u>atmosphere</u> of poverty and sadness. _____

14. It was difficult for the <u>tender-hearted</u> old man to control his naughty grandchildren because he hated to punish them. _____

15. On Halloween, as most children go trick or treating, some collect money for <u>charitable</u> causes. _____

Exercise C: True or False

Circle TRUE or FALSE for each statement.

16. Five hours of sleep a night will **suffice** for most people. . . . .   TRUE   FALSE

17. **Zealous** people work hard for what they believe in. . . .   TRUE   FALSE

18. A **windfall** is likely to result in an injury. . . . .   TRUE   FALSE

19. **Humanitarians** are selfish and greedy. . . . .   TRUE   FALSE

20. **Arduous** activities are tiring. . . . .   TRUE   FALSE

21. Metal **deteriorates** when it rusts. . . . .   TRUE   FALSE

22. A corkscrew has a **spiral** shape. . . . .   TRUE   FALSE

Exercise D: What It's Not

Write the Word that belongs in each blank.

23. A friendship that lasts for many years is NOT . . . . . . _____

24. A heart problem that is life-threatening is NOT . . . . _____

25. Naps, relaxing vacations, and easy jobs are NOT . . . . _____

26. Someone who is able to forgive and forget is NOT . . . . _____

27. A thick piece of fabric that blocks one's vision is NOT . . . . . _____

28. If a man feels full after a bite or two, his appetite is NOT . . . . _____

29. Someone who is open, honest, and straightforward is NOT . . . . _____

Exercise E: Questions

Write the Word that best answers the question.

30. What describes the shape of a spring? _____

31. What describes a cliff but not a gently sloping hill? _____

32. What is a word that means a mood or "feeling in the air"? _____

33. What do you do to an instruction or statement when you "put it another way"? _____

34. What do houses, cars, furnaces, and tools do if they're used but not taken care of? _____

35. What would describe an inheritance from a relative you didn't even know you had? _____

Exercise F: Fill-in

Write the **Word** that best completes each sentence.

36. A _____ of red ribbon made each white post look like a giant candy cane.

37. After an _____ day of carrying furniture up three flights of stairs, we were completely worn out.

38. My dad got a _____ at work—a big bonus that he hadn't known he'd get.

39. The mayor has been quite _____ about improving our city's schools, and his earnest and spirited efforts have paid off.

40. Winona's muscles had begun to _____ after many weeks without exercise.

41. Mother Teresa's reputation as a great _____ came from her many years of work helping poor people in India.

42. A surgeon will remove the lump; if it's _____, I won't need any further treatment.

43. The bruises on Peggy's legs showed through her _____ stockings.

44. Our joy over the goal that put us ahead was _____, for the other team scored almost immediately.

45. You don't use quotation marks if you _____ what someone says, but you should still give that person credit for the idea.

46. Ginger's mind was filled with _____ ideas about how to pay Benjy back for embarrassing her.

47. I hope one can of paint will _____; I don't have enough money for two.

48. There was a tense _____ in the room, as if everyone were waiting for something bad to happen.

49. The _____ appetite of a shark makes it constantly search for food.

50. A _____ thief managed to fool my aunt into trusting him with her money.

Quick LIST			
arduous ADJ.	**deteriorate** V.	**paraphrase** V., N.	**vengeful** ADJ.
aura N.	**fleeting** ADJ.	**sheer** ADJ.	**wily** ADJ.
benign ADJ.	**humanitarian** N., ADJ.	**spiral** ADJ., N.	**windfall** N.
	insatiable ADJ.	**suffice** V.	**zealous** ADJ.

Although some spirals may seem wily or even vengeful, most are benign.

Lesson 24 _____

anticipation *an•tiss•uh•PAY•shun* NOUN

an expectation or a looking forward to [They waited with *anticipation* for the announcement.]

assent *uh•SENT*

VERB to agree with a plan, opinion, or proposal [We can move the date of the bake sale if the other club members *assent*.]

NOUN an agreement or consent [Please indicate your *assent* by raising your hand.]

beseech *bee•SEECH* VERB

to ask (someone) earnestly for something; to beg [How can you just walk away from someone who *beseeches* you for help?]

candid *KAN•did* ADJECTIVE

1. honest and open [I asked my doctor to be *candid* with me about my condition.]

2. informal; not posed [Marie liked the *candid* photographs of her wedding the best.]

despicable *dess•PIK•uh•bul* ADJECTIVE

worthy of scorn; completely unworthy of respect [I think it was *despicable* of Lauren to cheat someone who trusted her.]

dowdy *DOW•dee* ADJECTIVE

unattractive in appearance, due to being boring, overly plain, and unfashionable or being untidy and shabby [Wearing several sweaters and a shawl made the old lady look warm but *dowdy*.]

ebb *EB* VERB

1. to flow back toward the sea; *said of the tide* [When the tide *ebbs*, we may find new shells.]

2. to become less; to weaken [He waited for the cheers to *ebb* before continuing his speech.]

egotist *EE•go•tist* NOUN

someone who has too high an opinion of himself or herself, is overly concerned with his or her own interests, and tends to think and talk too much about himself or herself [Sylvester is such an *egotist* that he assumed we were talking about him.]

empower *em•POW•ur* VERB

to give power to; to make able to act [The Constitution *empowers* Congress to make laws.]

fanatic *fuh•NAT•ik* NOUN

one who is overly and unreasonably enthusiastic about a belief; one who is carried away by devotion to something [Animal rights *fanatics* broke into the lab and freed the monkeys being used in the experiments.]

ingenuity *in•juh•NOO•uh•tee* NOUN

cleverness and originality [Cooper's *ingenuity* makes him able to solve problems in ways the rest of us have never considered trying.]

insubordinate *in•suh•BOR•duh•nit* ADJECTIVE

refusing to follow the orders of a person in authority [Darnell was fired for *insubordinate* behavior; he wouldn't do what the boss said.]

pertain *pur•TAIN* VERB

to have a necessary relationship to; to have to do with what is being discussed or considered [If your question *pertains* to the topic we are discussing, you may ask it.]

rebuff *ri•BUFF*

NOUN a clear refusal to accept assistance or advice that has been offered [My offer to help the woman with her boxes got a cold *rebuff*.]

VERB to refuse without making an effort to be polite; to turn down coldly and bluntly [When salespeople call at mealtime, I *rebuff* them.]

suave *SWAHV* ADJECTIVE

smooth and charming in manner; skillfully gracious [Nadia, who is quite *suave*, knows exactly how to react to a compliment.]

Candid Photo,
Candid Conversation 1

WOMAN: You are an egotist!
MAN: Why, thanks, but as I was just saying about my moustache, I believe . . .

Exercise A: What Is It?

Write the Word that each rhymed clue describes.

USE A WORD ONLY ONE
TIME IN EACH EXERCISE.

1. His manners are polished; he knows what to do.
   I'd say this describes him quite well, wouldn't you? _____

2. This person thinks that every look's a look of admiration.
   And he or she is often found "me-deep" in conversation. _____

3. This word describes those people, young or old,
   Who should, but will not, do as they are told. _____

4. In her support for her beliefs, no matter what they are,
   This person is extreme, and so she often goes too far. _____

5. If this word describes you, and no one's impressed,
   Your name won't be found on the list of "Best Dressed." _____

6. A woman who does this might say, "Oh, please!"
   And clasp her hands and drop down to her knees. _____

7. This can be a sense of either eagerness or dread
   That fills your mind when you consider things that lie ahead. _____

Exercise B: Antonyms

Write the Word that means the opposite of each underlined word or phrase.

8. The waters will <u>rise</u> but then begin to ___. _____

9. Some will <u>protest</u> the change, but most people will ___ to it. _____

10. They used to be <u>crude, clumsy, and ignorant</u>, but now they're ___. _____

11. I don't know if my suggestion will get a <u>warm welcome</u> or a ___. _____

12. Liz responded with <u>admirable</u> calm to the ___ attack on her. _____

13. I wanted to look <u>stylish and classy</u>, not ___. _____

WOMAN: You're also the biggest idiot I know!
MAN: . . . a really superb moustache like mine is empowering. When I . . .

Exercise C: Analogies

Write the letter of the word that completes the analogy.

___ 14. *inventor : ingenuity :: sprinter :*
A. track C. stopwatch
B. speed D. competition

___ 15. *brat : misbehavior :: egotist :*
A. hope C. conceit
B. ability D. dishonesty

___ 16. *request : beseech :: promise :*
A. vow C. remind
B. answer D. suggest

___ 17. *tiredness : yawn :: assent :*
A. nod C. frown
B. wave D. shudder

Exercise D: If . . .

Write the **Word** that best completes each sentence.

18. If someone has burning feelings for or against a thing and will go to extreme lengths to act on those feelings, that person is a . . . .

   _____

19. If someone buys a winter jacket in early fall or sets up a crib before the baby is born or studies for a test, that person's actions are based on . . . .

   _____

20. If someone wants pictures of people behaving naturally, without preparing themselves or saying "Cheese," those photos will be . . . .

   _____

21. If someone expects to be the center of attention and starts most sentences with "I" and lacks interest in other people, that person is a real . . . .

   _____

22. If someone wears dull colors, pays no attention to what looks good on him or her, and even looks sort of sloppy, that person's appearance is . . . . .

   _____

Exercise E: Yes or No

Circle YES or NO for each statement.

23. Should the details in an essay **pertain** to the main idea? . . . .   YES   NO

24. Do commercials try to make the demand for a product **ebb**? . . . . . .   YES   NO

25. Does a nation **empower** people by giving them the right to vote? . . .   YES   NO

26. Are **suave** people likely to make fools of themselves in public? . . . .   YES   NO

27. Does a **candid** remark reveal what the speaker really thinks? . . . . . .   YES   NO

28. Are kind or generous actions **despicable** things to do? . . . .   YES   NO

Exercise F: Synonyms

Write the **Word** that could be used in place of each underlined word or phrase. This exercise continues on the next page.

29. Please give me your <u>frank and sincere</u> opinion.   _____

30. The patient's strength began to <u>fade</u> as he got sicker.   _____

31. The architect was praised for her <u>skillful imagination</u>.   _____

32. How does that witness's testimony <u>connect</u> to the case?   _____

Candid 2

BEGGAR:
I beseech you, ma'am, for a dime, a nickel, perhaps a quarter.

LADY:
Wouldn't you prefer a dollar?

BEGGAR:
No, ma'am, the change will do me good.

33. Education can help to <u>give strength and control to</u> people. _____

34. Clark fears that Lana will <u>coldly reject</u> him if he asks her out. _____

35. The coach kicked three members off the team for being <u>rebellious</u>. _____

Exercise G: Fill-in
Write the Word that best completes each sentence.

36. Stealing from children seems a particularly _____ thing to do.

37. The army will not put up with _____ conduct, so soldiers must obey commands.

38. Martin is likely to _____ my guidance; he's always determined to do things his own way.

39. Renaldo is so _____ that he knows what fork to use, what comment to make, and how to impress people.

40. Ads that _____ to available jobs are found in the newspaper's "Help Wanted" section.

41. Lucia's _____ showed in her use of inexpensive materials to create wonderful and original products.

42. Please be _____ about my performance; I want to know the truth.

43. Mrs. Roberts is a _____ about cleanliness and won't allow anyone to wear shoes in the house.

44. Jess used to be sort of _____, but lately she's been wearing some lovely outfits.

45. Conner is quite an obvious _____; all the pictures in his apartment are of himself.

46. I hope my folks will give their _____ to the arrangements I made for the party.

47. Enthusiasm for the team began to _____ as people realized how bad it was.

48. Kyeesha looked in the mailbox daily in _____ of a birthday check from her grandparents.

49. To me, it was an emergency, but I had to _____ my sister to let me use her bike.

50. I figure that learning to use a computer will _____ me to handle many jobs.

Candid 3
MOM: Can you fix the electrical outlet there in the den? You have such ingenuity.

TRUDY (in the den, a few moments later): NNNAAAHHHH!

MOM: Well, just say no. You don't need to rebuff me so!

Quick LIST
anticipation N.
assent V., N.
beseech V.
candid ADJ.
despicable ADJ.
dowdy ADJ.
ebb V.
egotist N.
empower V.
fanatic N.
ingenuity N.
insubordinate ADJ.
pertain V.
rebuff N., V.
suave ADJ.

Lesson 25

altercation *all•tur•KAY•shun* NOUN

an angry argument that may or may not include physical violence [There was an *altercation* between two drivers after one backed his car into the other's.]

attain *uh•TAIN* VERB

to arrive at or reach; to gain by effort [Toby worked really hard all year to *attain* his high math scores.]

contrite *kun•TRITE* ADJECTIVE

sorry about having done something wrong; regretful [Sarah was *contrite* about having disobeyed her father.]

decrepit *di•KREP•it* ADJECTIVE

broken down or worn out by age, illness, or use [Sam's *decrepit* desk collapsed when he slammed his books down on it.]

entreaty *en•TREET•ee* NOUN

a strong request; a plea [The teacher wasn't moved by our *entreaty* for additional time to finish our papers.]

grueling *GROOL•ing* ADJECTIVE

physically or mentally demanding [After an extremely *grueling* hike, everyone collapsed on the ground in exhaustion.]

hanker *HANK•ur* VERB

to have a strong desire or wish [The one thing that Linda *hankers* for most of all is a horse of her own.]

inadvertent *in•ad•VERT•unt* ADJECTIVE

due to carelessness or a failure to pay attention; not intentional [Leaving the gate open was Kerri's fault, but it was *inadvertent*; she just didn't check the latch.]

laud *LAWD* VERB

to praise, especially to praise highly ["Even though you didn't succeed this time," said my mom, "I *laud* your effort."]

misgiving *mis•GIV•ing* NOUN

a feeling of doubt or worry [Juana stepped onto the creaky old bridge with *misgiving*.]

---

obscure *ub•SKYOOR*

ADJECTIVE **1.** not clear or distinct [An *obscure* shape in the dark alley looked threatening until I saw that it was just an old ironing board.]

ADJECTIVE **2.** not famous or well-known; attracting little notice [Marcus was an *obscure* stage actor before he starred in last year's biggest movie.]

VERB to conceal from view; to hide [Sue scribbled through the word to try to *obscure* it.]

NOTE: A word may have several meanings, as is the case with *obscure* (which has even more meanings than are given here). Don't let this scare you away from a word. The meanings are often closely related to each other. *Obscure* always has to do with things that are not clear, either to the senses or to the mind.

---

placate *PLAY•kate* VERB

to ease someone's or something's anger; to calm [Since I was late for work yesterday, I put in extra effort to try to *placate* my boss.]

rambunctious *ram•BUNK•shuss* ADJECTIVE

very lively; wild; disorderly [One group of people got too *rambunctious* and were asked to leave the restaurant.]

tremor *TREM•ur* NOUN

a slight shaking movement; trembling [I felt a *tremor* in my knees as I began my speech.]

woebegone *WOH•bee•gone* ADJECTIVE

looking sad or mournful [The little girl's *woebegone* face broke my heart.]

Exercise A: Synonyms

Write the Word that is a synonym for each set of words.

USE A WORD ONLY ONE TIME IN EACH EXERCISE.

1. uneasiness; fear; distrust _____

2. acquire; gain; achieve _____

3. miserable; unhappy; gloomy _____

4. dim; faint; vague _____

5. difficult; exhausting; hard _____

6. accidental; thoughtless; unplanned _____

7. ashamed; sorry; apologetic _____

Exercise B: Matching

Match each phrase on the left to the phrase on the right that means the same, or nearly the same, thing.

____ 8. *laud* a lawyer

____ 9. temporary *tremor*

____ 10. *placate* a politician

____ 11. *rambunctious* reception

____ 12. alarming *altercation*

____ 13. *hanker* for a home

____ 14. *decrepit* dwelling

A. short shudder

B. frightening fight

C. desire a dwelling

D. applaud an attorney

E. rickety residence

F. soothe a senator

G. wild welcome

Exercise C: Rhyme Time

Write the Word that best completes each rhyme. This exercise continues on the next page.

15. If you refuse to use your brain,
There won't be much you can ___. _____

16. Because I'd really like to go on living,
I viewed the reckless plan with some ___. _____

17. I never should have lied. It wasn't right.
My conscience bothers me; I feel ___. _____

18. You've never heard of her, I am quite sure.
She's written books, but they are all ___. _____

A black car, its headlights turned off, was traveling along a dark country road. The moon and stars were not visible, and lights on the nearest farm were a mile away. Still, a farmer standing out in the middle of his field had no trouble seeing the car. He even recognized and waved to the driver.

Question:
Why weren't the car and driver too obscure for the farmer to see?

Answer:
It was a bright and sunny day.

19. "He started it!" Now, there's an accusation
    That's common after any ___.   _____

20. You said this work was easy. Were you fooling?
    Or were you unaware that it was ___.   _____

Exercise D: Antonyms

Write the **Word** that means the opposite of each
underlined word or phrase.

21. Her speeches always <u>criticize</u> her opponent and ___
    her own accomplishments.   _____

22. The winner's expression was <u>joyful</u>; the loser's was ___.   _____

23. A <u>demand</u> will get you nowhere, but a sincere ___ might work.   _____

24. Brad hoped for a <u>peaceful discussion</u> with Julia, not another ___.   _____

25. Some children were <u>quiet and well-behaved</u>, but others were ___.   _____

26. Excuses will only <u>further enrage</u> Mom; an apology might ___ her.   _____

27. I know that the sunrise will <u>reveal</u> what night and darkness ___.   _____

28. Please use a <u>sturdy</u> ladder; you won't be safe on that ___ one.   _____

29. Leaving Lenny off the list wasn't <u>intentional</u>; it was ___.   _____

30. I thought my new job would be <u>effortless</u>, but it's ___.   _____

Exercise E: Put It Briefly

Write the **Word** that best completes each sentence.

31. The man's appeal for help was stronger than just an expression of
    mild desire. It came from his heart and included phrases such as
    "Please, oh, please!" and "I beg you!" *Briefly,* it was an . . . .   _____

32. The dogs chased each other around the room, barked loudly, tore up
    the garbage, and knocked over the chairs. *Briefly,* they were . . . . .   _____

33. I *really* want a bike. I can't get the idea out of my head. I itch for one.
    I yearn for one. *Briefly,* a bike is something for which I . . . .   _____

34. The porch's railing is wobbly. The floor boards are so old and rotten
    my foot would go right through them. *Briefly,* the porch is . . . .   _____

35. The ground suddenly didn't seem solid. There was no big quake, just
    a sort of vibration, like a shiver. *Briefly,* what I felt was a . . . .   _____

Quick LIST

alteration N.	decrepit ADJ.	inadvertent ADJ.	placate V.
attain V.	entreaty N.	laud V.	rambunctious ADJ.
contrite ADJ.	grueling ADJ.	misgiving N.	tremor N.
	hanker V.	obscure ADJ., V.	woebegone ADJ.

Exercise F: Fill-in

Write the Word that best completes each sentence.

Question:
Why did the famous, prize-winning farmer become so obscure when he went in to take his nap?

Answer: He wasn't out standing in his field.

36. The clubhouse may look shabby and _____ now, but wait until you see how we fix it up.

37. I gave in to my little brother's _____ that he be allowed to go with me.

38. Reba was so determined to _____ a position on the basketball team that she put in many hours of practice.

39. When the children got _____, I read them a story to try to calm them down.

40. After a long and _____ day of fighting the forest fire, Masako was completely worn out.

41. I knew that the _____ in my hands revealed to everyone how nervous I was.

42. All the kids _____ for this new shoe style now, but who knows what they'll want next year?

43. As the _____ got louder and more intense, we worried that the boys might hurt each other.

44. Ramona was _____ about hurting Sandi's feelings and asked to be forgiven.

45. I felt a strong _____ about walking down the path in the dark, but I took a deep breath and started out.

46. We visited some _____ little towns on back roads that weren't even on the map.

47. With a sob and a _____ look, the little boy watched his balloon sail away into the clouds.

48. Danny's rudeness was _____; he would never be so impolite on purpose.

49. There will be no way to _____ Brooke if you lose her new bat, so be careful with it.

50. Why did so many movie critics _____ that film when it was so bad?

One More Bumper Sticker

CONSCIOUSNESS
THE GRUELING TIME
BETWEEN NAPS

Word Fun 5!

Naming

Match each name to the description it goes best with.

____ 1. Hank Urr   A. She's kind of falling apart.

____ 2. Ms. Givving   B. If he has it, everyone wants it.

____ 3. Dee Krepput   C. He likes to help the unfortunate.

____ 4. Pop Yoolurize   D. She tends to be filled with doubts.

____ 5. Auntie Sippation   E. She's always thinking of the future.

____ 6. Hugh Manitarian   F. He's always longing for something.

Defining

Match the invented

____ 1. *deterrierate*

____ 2. *flocktuate*

____ 3. *optimom*

____ 4. *beenign*

____ 5. *slapdish*

____ 6. *funatic*

Puzzling

Identify the **Word** from Unit 5 that fits the clue in each box.

1. d _____

 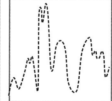

3. e _____

2. h _____

4. f _____

Digging

Find and underline the **Word** from Unit 5 that is buried in each sentence. The words to dig up are *assent, candid, laud,* and *reverie.*

1. There was a full auditorium of people who wanted to praise and honor the hero.

2. Because the wait seemed to go on forever, I entertained myself by daydreaming.

3. When the teacher proposed a field trip, everyone in the class enthusiastically agreed.

4. Honest, straight talk can be like a tonic, and I dished it out in the hope it would help her.

Sheer Stupidity or Wily Ingenuity?

A zealous locksmith
died of late
And made his way to
Heaven's gate.
He stood outside and
did not knock
Because he planned to
pick the lock.

word to its meaning.

A. someone who is crazy about games, parties, and amusement

B. how a table looks when it's been carelessly set for dinner

C. what a group of sheep do as their numbers rise and fall

D. what a male bee is (since male bees have no stingers)

E. what certain dogs do as they get older and weaker

F. what the very best mother's skills and efforts are

Searching
Circle the words that go from left to right or top to bottom to find answers to the clues below.

1. How a person with a woebegone expression looks

2. The kind of light that makes things obscure

3. An animal that's known for being wily

4. Another word for *arduous*

5. What a nation's aggression may cause

6. What you want to get if you are vengeful

7. What a dog with an insatiable appetite may become

S	L	E	E	P	H	B
M	O	U	S	E	A	R
A	G	O	F	A	T	I
D	I	M	O	S	H	G
S	A	D	X	Y	I	H
C	S	E	V	E	N	T
W	A	R	H	A	R	D

Rhyming
Make each poem rhyme and have a poetic rhythm by substituting a **Word** from Unit 5 for the underlined words.

1. Be sure to watch that waiter; it's a rarity
   For someone to reveal that much <u>skill in movement</u>. _____

2. "No, thank you" would have surely been enough.
   You didn't need to snarl in your <u>refusal of assistance</u>. _____

3. The earthquake caused our town a lot of trouble
   By turning lots of buildings into <u>broken bits and pieces</u>. _____

4. Shampoo instructions say to lather twice.
   I just don't get it. Won't one time <u>be all that is needed</u>? _____

Lesson 26

acclimate *AK•luh•mate* VERB

to adjust to a new climate, situation, environment, or condition [It may take a while for Alfredo to *acclimate* to the new school.]

acme *AK•mee* NOUN

highest point [Some athletes do not reach the *acme* of their power until they are in their late twenties.]

breadth *BREDTH* NOUN

1. size from side to side; width [It's difficult for Lucius to find a suit that will fit properly because of the *breadth* of his shoulders.]

Breadth from weights

2. range or extent; lack of narrowness [Carmen has held many jobs over her career, and the *breadth* of her experience is impressive.]

dally *DAL•ee* VERB

1. to deal lightly and carelessly (with) [I'm a little concerned that Abigail will *dally* with Pasha's feelings.]

2. to waste time or let it pass without concern [If you continue to *dally*, we'll be late.]

elapse *ee•LAPS* VERB

to go by or pass; *said of time* [Precious days may *elapse* while the rest of us wait for you to make up your mind.]

elation *ee•LAY•shun* NOUN

great joy; high spirits [Hearing that he had won the prize filled Howard with *elation*.]

feisty *FICE•tee* ADJECTIVE

showing courage, energy, and a readiness to respond to a quarrel [Phoebe's *feisty* little dog chased the bigger one out of the yard.]

infamous *IN•fuh•muss* ADJECTIVE

well known for something bad [Bonnie Parker and Clyde Barrow were *infamous* bank robbers in the 1930s.]

jut *JUT* VERB

to stick out from the main body of something [Beware of the shelf that *juts* out from the wall.]

literal *LIT•ur•ul* ADJECTIVE

dealing with fact or basic meaning, without exaggeration or the imaginative use of words; exact ["I rolled on the floor with laughter" is a *literal* statement only if the speaker had actually been rolling on the floor.]

noncommittal *non•kuh•MIT•ul* ADJECTIVE

not willing to promise; not revealing one's purpose, intention, or feelings [When I asked my mom whether I would be getting a new bicycle for my birthday, she responded with a *noncommittal* gesture.]

perceptive *pur•SEP•tiv* ADJECTIVE

able to take in something with the mind easily and quickly; good at both noticing details and understanding their meaning [It was quite *perceptive* of Zak to realize that Andrea wasn't unfriendly but just timid.]

placid *PLASS•id* ADJECTIVE

undisturbed; calm [Cows are usually quite *placid* creatures.]

requisite *REK•wuh•zit*

ADJECTIVE required by the situation [Does Dorothy have the *requisite* skills for the job?]

NOUN something that is required by the situation [Good balance is a *requisite* for a tightrope walker.]

Two sports, one placid, one not so much

revelation *rev•uh•LAY•shun* NOUN

1. something revealed or made known, especially when it had been hidden or secret [We were interested by Shari's *revelation* that she had been a champion diver.]

2. a surprising discovery [Reporters were eager for the jury's *revelation* of its verdict.]

Exercise A: Opposites

Write the Word that best completes each sentence.

USE A WORD ONLY ONE
TIME IN EACH EXERCISE.

1. No one can get a rise out of Johnny. He's patient, good-tempered, and a bit timid. He puts up with just about anything, avoids trouble, and backs off from quarrels. Donny, on the other hand, is . . . .

2. Carol is at the absolute bottom of her acting career. She doesn't get the good acting jobs she used to and doesn't earn nearly as much money as she once did. However, Merrill's career is at its . . . .

3. Everyone knew who Dilbert was and admired and respected him. He was honored for his good deeds, kind heart, wisdom, and greatness. Everyone knew who Gilbert was too, but he was . . . .

4. Marlene is efficient. She bustles around, doing things quickly. She never puts anything off and always keeps one eye on the clock. Doreen, however, tends to . . . .

5. When Paul is angry, he says he's steamed. When he's hungry, he "can eat a horse." He refers to clumsy people as being "all thumbs." Saul doesn't understand him because Saul is always . . . .

Exercise B: Synonyms

Write the Word that could be used in place of each underlined word or phrase.

6. The smooth, quiet lake had a surface like a mirror.

7. The broadness of Andrew's knowledge impressed us.

8. These peaches are at the peak of their ripe, juicy perfection.

9. Pam gave a long but precise and accurate report of the event.

10. A clever and observant person can tell when a friend is upset.

11. Let's not allow another year to slip away before we meet again.

12. Don't mess around with me; treat me seriously and with respect.

13. My ears poke out from the side of my head like two cup handles.

14. I don't think a separate salad fork is a necessity for eating dinner.

15. Fans responded with delighted excitement to the team's victory.

16. When winter comes, some animals change to be suitable for it by growing thicker fur.

17. Voters were startled by the newspaper's announcement about the mayor's past.

Exercise C: Completion

Choose the correct answer to complete each sentence.

_____ 18. A common response to a **revelation** is
A. "Oh, my!"   B. "Yes, I know."   C. "That's ridiculous!"

_____ 19. An example of a **noncommittal** answer is
A. "No way!"   B. "We'll see."   C. "Yes, for sure."

_____ 20. Something that can **elapse** is
A. a week.   B. a joke.   C. an illness.

_____ 21. A thing that might **jut** into a lake is
A. a pier.   B. a diver.   C. pollution.

_____ 22. Sounds that might indicate a feeling of **elation** are
A. sobs.   B. boos.   C. cheers.

Dribbling—a
requisite in
some activities,
a side effect in
others

Exercise D: What Is It?

Write the Word that each clue describes.

23. This kind of horse is unlikely to throw its rider.   _____

24. People do this as they get used to a new way of life.   _____

25. This describes politicians who won't state their views.   _____

26. This describes people who are sensitive and have sharp minds.   _____

27. When something is essential for some purpose, this describes it.   _____

28. To find a rectangle's area, you must know both its length and this.   _____

29. This kind of person is hard to push around and would make a bully regret trying.   _____

30. This describes a criminal whose picture is on the front page of every newspaper.   _____

Exercise E: Yes or No

Circle YES or NO for each statement.

31. Are **placid** people likely to lose their tempers? . . . . .   YES   NO

32. Are wise people likely to be **perceptive**? . . . .   YES   NO

33. Is a racquet a **requisite** for tennis? . . . .   YES   NO

34. Do runners **dally** when a race begins? . . . .   YES   NO

35. Do streets have more **breadth** than sidewalks? . . . .   YES   NO

A pleasant
way to dally

Exercise F: Fill-in

Write the **Word** that best completes each sentence.

36. I prefer to _____ myself to the cold water gradually rather than to jump right in.

37. The _____ translation of *adieu* is "to God," but French people use this word to mean "goodbye."

38. Cindy was _____ about whether or not she would try out for the volleyball team.

39. Jerome expressed his _____ by saying that he felt on top of the world.

40. My new baby sister is very _____; she just lies in her crib and coos, and she'll let anyone pick her up and hold her.

41. Katya's comments were quite _____; they got right to the heart of the matter.

42. Everyone was eager to hear the candidate's _____ about whom he had chosen as his running mate.

43. Many people would agree that one of the most _____ leaders of all time was Adolph Hitler.

44. We had to open a gate that went across the _____ of the lane before we could drive on.

45. Dorothy has completed all of the _____ courses to earn her college degree.

46. While an elephant's tusks _____ outward, a walrus's curve downward.

47. If you let all of Saturday _____ without starting on your homework, you'll have a lot to do on Sunday.

48. During the _____ of the band's popularity, every one of its concerts was sold out.

49. I like to _____ with painting, but I am not interested in trying to make a career out of it.

50. Grandma gets _____ when anyone criticizes the way she dresses, so don't say anything negative about her bowling skills unless you're looking for a fight.

Elation from elevation

Bowling night— the acme of Grandma's week

Quick LIST	**dally** V.	**infamous** ADJ.	**perceptive** ADJ.
acclimate V.	**elapse** V.	**jut** V.	**placid** ADJ.
acme N.	**elation** N.	**literal** ADJ.	**requisite** ADJ., N.
breadth N.	**feisty** ADJ.	**noncommittal** ADJ.	**revelation** N.

Lesson 27

allot *uh•LOT* VERB

to distribute in shares; to provide a part of something to each member of a group [Why did the chairperson *allot* Heather ten minutes to speak and me only five?]

bland *BLAND* ADJECTIVE

mild and agreeable but without interesting characteristics [While Olivia's stomach was upset, she could eat only *bland* food, like mashed potatoes.]

contend *kun•TEND* VERB

1. to state as a fact, often in argument with a conflicting statement or belief [You say that you earned the money, but Quincy *contends* that you borrowed it from him.]

2. to struggle (against something) in an effort, fight, or competition; to deal with [To make it across the lake, we had to *contend* with harsh winds and heavy waves.]

3. to compete [The semifinalists will *contend* for the championship tomorrow.]

dauntless *DAWNT•luss* ADJECTIVE

not able to be frightened or discouraged [The *dauntless* team didn't seem worried about their larger and stronger opponents.]

discrepancy *dis•KREP•un•see* NOUN

lack of agreement or consistency; a difference [There's a *discrepancy* between the money in the cash register and the record of sales.]

enunciate *ee•NUN•see•ate* VERB

to pronounce clearly [Oscar's mouth was full, so he couldn't *enunciate* very well.]

exult *eg•ZULT* VERB

to rejoice greatly [Sharif is sure to *exult* in Tanya's victory because he worked very hard on her campaign.]

outmoded *out•MO•did* ADJECTIVE

no longer in fashion or common use; old-fashioned [Some people feel that Ms. Hoppe's training methods are *outmoded*.]

pungent *pun•JUNT* ADJECTIVE

noticeably strong or sharp in taste or smell [The stew was *pungent* with garlic.]

stickler *STIK•lur* NOUN

a person who insists on doing things in exactly the right way [My teacher is a *stickler* for the rules; she calls the roll even when she already knows we're all present.]

stupendous *stoo•PEN•duss* ADJECTIVE

astonishing; overwhelming [Mae-Lin gasped when she heard the *stupendous* news.]

subterfuge *SUB•tur•fyooj* NOUN

any action or plan used to hide one's real purpose or to avoid a difficulty [Putting pillows under the blankets was a *subterfuge* to make it appear that someone was in the bed.]

symmetrical *suh•MET•ruh•kul* ADJECTIVE

exactly alike or very similar in form or arrangement on both sides of a dividing line or central area; balanced [Hang one small painting on each side of the big one so that the arrangement looks *symmetrical*.]

vicarious *vy•KAIR•ee•us* ADJECTIVE

felt as if one were experiencing something that another is experiencing [Watching Jeremy open his gifts gave me *vicarious* pleasure.]

vice *VICE* NOUN

1. a fault, weakness, or failing [A tendency to exaggerate is one of her *vices*.]

2. evil actions, habits, or characteristics; wicked behavior [Illegal gambling is part of the *vice* problem in many cities.]

I need advice from someone nice.
Is it a vice to say things twice?
I need advice from someone nice.
Is it a vice to say things twice?

Exercise A: Yes or No

Circle YES or NO for each statement.

1. Do butterfly wings tend to be *symmetrical*? . . . .   YES   NO
2. Do runners in a race *contend* with each other? . . . .   YES   NO
3. Would a careless, sloppy worker be called a *stickler*? . . . .   YES   NO
4. If you think a movie was *stupendous*, did you find it boring? . . . .   YES   NO
5. Can you have a *vicarious* experience while watching a TV show? . . . .   YES   NO
6. Is there a *discrepancy* between Face A and Face B (below)? . . . .   YES   NO
7. Might people yell "Yippee!" to show that they *exult*? . . . .   YES   NO
8. Are skunks capable of producing a *pungent* odor? . . . .   YES   NO
9. Do bullies hope their victims will be *dauntless*? . . . .   YES   NO

Exercise B: Synonyms

Write the **Word** that is a synonym for each set of words.

10. incredible; amazing; extraordinary   _____

11. trick; deception; scheme   _____

12. imperfection; sin; flaw   _____

13. blah; dull; flavorless   _____

14. argue; insist; declare   _____

15. fearless; bold; confident   _____

16. divide up; give out; assign   _____

A

Exercise C: Antonyms

Write the **Word** that is an antonym for each set of words.

17. excellence; purity; morality   _____

18. cowardly; timid; gutless   _____

19. give up; surrender; quit   _____

20. mourn; regret; grieve   _____

21. uneven; crooked; lopsided   _____

22. modern; up-to-date; current   _____

B

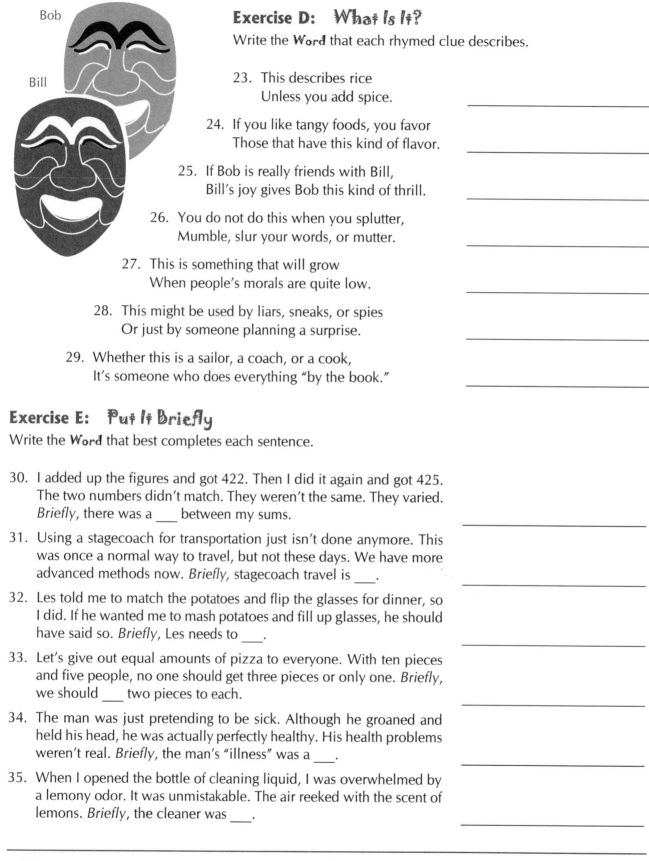

Bob

Bill

Exercise D: What Is It?

Write the **Word** that each rhymed clue describes.

23. This describes rice
    Unless you add spice.

    _____

24. If you like tangy foods, you favor
    Those that have this kind of flavor.

    _____

25. If Bob is really friends with Bill,
    Bill's joy gives Bob this kind of thrill.

    _____

26. You do not do this when you splutter,
    Mumble, slur your words, or mutter.

    _____

27. This is something that will grow
    When people's morals are quite low.

    _____

28. This might be used by liars, sneaks, or spies
    Or just by someone planning a surprise.

    _____

29. Whether this is a sailor, a coach, or a cook,
    It's someone who does everything "by the book."

    _____

Exercise E: Put It Briefly

Write the **Word** that best completes each sentence.

30. I added up the figures and got 422. Then I did it again and got 425. The two numbers didn't match. They weren't the same. They varied. *Briefly,* there was a ___ between my sums.

31. Using a stagecoach for transportation just isn't done anymore. This was once a normal way to travel, but not these days. We have more advanced methods now. *Briefly,* stagecoach travel is ___.

32. Les told me to match the potatoes and flip the glasses for dinner, so I did. If he wanted me to mash potatoes and fill up glasses, he should have said so. *Briefly,* Les needs to ___.

33. Let's give out equal amounts of pizza to everyone. With ten pieces and five people, no one should get three pieces or only one. *Briefly,* we should ___ two pieces to each.

34. The man was just pretending to be sick. Although he groaned and held his head, he was actually perfectly healthy. His health problems weren't real. *Briefly,* the man's "illness" was a ___.

35. When I opened the bottle of cleaning liquid, I was overwhelmed by a lemony odor. It was unmistakable. The air reeked with the scent of lemons. *Briefly,* the cleaner was ___.

Exercise F: Fill-in

Write the **Word** that best completes each sentence.

36. The _____ little shepherd puppy flung herself at the huge intruder.

37. This _____ room needs some pictures or bright colors to liven it up.

38. There was a _____ between the advertised price and the price I was charged, so I want a refund.

39. Telegrams are _____ as a form of communication, but at one time every town had its own telegraph office.

40. We'll have to _____ with traffic jams and crowds if we try to go shopping today.

41. Petra is such a _____ for the truth that she won't even tell a little fib to be polite.

42. The musical was a _____ success, and the theater was packed for months.

43. Connie winced with _____ pain when the car door slammed on Lorenzo's hand.

44. The school decided to _____ each senior ten tickets for the graduation ceremony.

45. Dad says my laziness is a _____ that will cause me many problems.

46. The house was completely _____; the right side was a mirror image of the left side.

47. Crowds gathered in the street to _____ when peace was declared.

48. My grandma's soup has a peppery, _____ taste that is quite pleasant.

49. Wearing a deliveryman's uniform was a _____ that allowed the burglar to get past the guards.

50. Mrs. Weitzman spoke slowly, taking care to _____ every word.

Exercise G: Writing

How would you complete the following sentence? "I **contend** that ___ will be totally **outmoded** one hundred years from now." Copy the sentence onto your own paper. Then fill in the blank with a word or phrase that you think is appropriate, and explain your answer. Use at least THREE **Words**.

Quick LIST

allot V.
bland ADJ.
contend V.
dauntless ADJ.
discrepancy N.
enunciate V.
exult V.
outmoded ADJ.
pungent ADJ.
stickler N.
stupendous ADJ.
subterfuge N.
symmetrical ADJ.
vicarious ADJ.
vice N.

I **hope** that war
Will be outmoded,
Bombs destroyed
And guns unloaded,
"Peace on Earth"
At last decoded.

Lesson 28 _____

adept *uh•DEPT* ADJECTIVE

highly skillful [Even people who are quite *adept* at cutting hair usually aren't able to cut their own very well.]

ambiguity *am•buh•GYOO•uh•tee* NOUN

having more than one possible meaning [The *ambiguity* of "You can't spend too much" left us wondering if we shouldn't spend very much or if no amount would be too much.]

besiege *bee•SEEJ* VERB

1. to surround with armed forces and attack in order to capture or force a surrender [When an army *besieges* a town, no one is able to get in or out safely.]

2. to crowd around [As soon as the game ends, photographers will *besiege* the winning team to try to get pictures.]

3. to overwhelm with questions or requests [If listeners *besiege* a radio station asking that a certain song be played, the station will probably play it frequently.]

censure *SEN•shur*

VERB to express strong disapproval [The principal will *censure* those who cheated.]

NOUN an expression of strong disapproval [The defendant was lucky to get off with just a *censure* from the judge for his actions.]

Question:

Why was the nose-drop saleswoman censured for trying to get people to use her product?

Answer: She kept sticking her business into other people's noses.

credible *KRED•uh•bul* ADJECTIVE

easy to believe or have faith in [Otto gave a *credible* excuse for being late, so we couldn't be angry with him.]

dogmatic *dog•MAT•ik* ADJECTIVE

holding strongly to certain opinions or beliefs; unreasonably insistent that one's own views are correct [Harold made his attitudes very clear in his *dogmatic* declarations.]

emulate *EM•yoo•late* VERB

to try to be like someone one admires; to try to equal; to copy the behavior of [We often try to *emulate* our heroes.]

ill-advised *ill•ad•VIZED* ADJECTIVE

showing a lack of careful thought; unwise [Don't you think that leaving the door unlocked all day was rather *ill-advised*?]

irreparable *ih•REP•ur•uh•bul* ADJECTIVE

not able to be repaired [The gossip did *irreparable* damage to Jasper's reputation.]

marital *MAIR•ih•tul* ADJECTIVE

having to do with marriage [If the form asks your *marital* status, write "single."]

noteworthy *NOTE•wur•thee* ADJECTIVE

worthy of attention; important [A number of different scientists made *noteworthy* contributions to the discovery.]

ornery *OR•nur•ee* or *ORN•ree* ADJECTIVE

hard to get along with; mean and stubborn [You may want to avoid Uncle Alfred today; he seems to be in an *ornery* mood.]

preen *PREEN* VERB

1. to clean, trim, and arrange feathers with the beak; *said of birds* [Watch those cardinals *preen* themselves.]

2. to dress with great care; to check and arrange the details of one's appearance [Before my older sister Claudette goes out for the evening, she always *preens* for an hour—or two or three.]

prevalent *PREV•uh•lunt* ADJECTIVE

widely occurring, existing, practiced, or accepted [The use of backpacks is *prevalent* among students today.]

scrutinize *SKROOT•un•ize* VERB

to look at something long and carefully [A good carpenter will *scrutinize* the plans for a building before starting to construct it.]

Exercise A: Questions
Write the **Word** that best answers the question.

1. What might a worker receive
   if the boss finds him or her sleeping on the job?   _____

2. What do people often do before going out on a date?   _____

3. What describes a person who does a thing easily and well? _____

4. What kind of vows do people make during their wedding? _____

5. What do soldiers sometimes do to enemies' forts?   _____

6. What describes a mule that kicks and bites?   _____

Exercise B: Matching
Match each phrase on the left to the phrase on the right that means the same, or nearly the same, thing.

Scrooge was scrutinizing his financial records for errors his clerk might have made. He was disturbed, however, by an annoying humming sound. Ornery and disagreeable as usual, Scrooge bellowed, "Who is making that awful racket?"

A cricket, furious at this terrible censure, bellowed

back, "*Racket*? I beg your pardon, sir, but that was music! I am quite adept at making music!"

"That is not a credible claim!" replied Scrooge dogmatically. "You simply repeated the same bar of music over and over!"

"Naturally," the cricket said. "I thought you, of all people, would understand. I'm a bar hum bug!" ■

_____ 7. **adept** at adding

_____ 8. **noteworthy** news

_____ 9. **emulate** educators

_____ 10. **scrutinize** scratches

_____ 11. **prevalent** poverty

_____ 12. **censure** students

_____ 13. **dogmatic** dope

A. narrow-minded nitwit

B. masterful at math

C. widespread want

D. study scrapes

E. imitate instructors

F. remarkable report

G. soundly scold scholars

Exercise C: Antonyms
Write the **Word** that is an antonym for each set of words.

14. smart; practical; sensible   _____

15. pleasant; agreeable; friendly   _____

16. correctable; fixable; reversible _____

17. flexible; accepting; open-minded _____

18. clearness; precision; certainty   _____

19. clumsy; fumbling; awkward   _____

20. uncommon; unusual; rare   _____

Exercise D: Synonyms

Write the **Word** that could be used in place of each underlined word or phrase.

21. People who supported the bill began to <u>flood</u> the governor's office with mail.

_____

22. Younger children often attempt to <u>follow the example of</u> their older brothers and sisters.

_____

23. Intelligent and calm, the woman made a <u>convincing</u> witness.

_____

24. Randy's <u>outstanding</u> accomplishments made us all proud of him.

_____

25. The couple hoped to exist in a state of <u>wedded</u> happiness forever.

_____

26. How long do you intend to <u>groom yourself</u> in front of the mirror?

_____

27. Polly was <u>foolish</u> to be rude to someone she wants a favor from.

_____

28. Nathaniel stopped to <u>carefully examine</u> one of the paintings.

_____

Exercise E: Other Forms of Words

Use what you know about the **Words** to choose the correct answers.

_____ 29. An **ambiguous** statement would be difficult to
    A. hear.   B. repeat.   C. understand.

_____ 30. People have great **credibility** if they are known for being
    A. funny.   B. honest.   C. hot-tempered.

_____ 31. It would require **scrutiny** to look for something
    A. tiny.   B. cheap.   C. dangerous.

Exercise F: Put It Briefly

Write the **Word** that best completes each sentence.
This exercise continues on the next page.

32. When a big trial is going on, dozens of reporters often cluster at the court. In the hallway, they gather around the defendant and lawyers and even block their way. *Briefly*, reporters ___ them.

_____

33. Laurie's relationship with Myrna is ruined. They had a fight that they can't get over. Their friendship was destroyed so completely that it cannot recover, no matter what. *Briefly*, the harm was ___.

_____

34. The story Drew told made perfect sense. What he said had happened was not only possible, it was likely, and I assumed that what he told me was what really occurred. *Briefly*, his story was ___.

_____

Ill-Advised Projects for the School Science Fair

What do you get if you cross . . .
1. a cow with some grass seed?
2. a book of synonyms with a dinosaur?
3. a chicken with a guitar?
4. a cheap microphone with a cricket?

Answers:
1. A lawn mooer
2. Tyranno-thesaurus
3. A chicken that makes music when you pluck it
4. An annoying humming sound

35. Headlines can be confusing. What does "Fireman Helps Dog Bite Victim" mean? And how about "City Council Can't Stop Gambling"? These statements are simply unclear. Each one can mean two very different things! *Briefly*, they show ___.

_____

Exercise G: Fill-in
Write the Word that best completes each sentence.

Quick LIST

adept ADJ.
ambiguity N.
besiege V.
censure V., N.
credible ADJ.
dogmatic ADJ.
emulate V.
ill-advised ADJ.
irreparable ADJ.
marital ADJ.
noteworthy ADJ.
ornery ADJ.
preen V.
prevalent ADJ.
scrutinize V.

_____

"Bah, humbug! If I had a microphone, I'd give you a real humming!"

36. Fans often _____ the players as they arrive for a game and when they leave, asking for autographs.

37. Two-story houses are _____ in this part of town, but there are a few one-story ones.

38. Using certain drugs can result in _____ injury to the human body.

39. A handwriting expert was asked to _____ the signature to see if it was a forgery.

40. Fiona watched everything Teri did so she could _____ the other girl's actions.

41. Luis is so _____ at juggling that he's able to keep six oranges in the air at a time.

42. The Senate voted to _____ one of its members for using campaign funds illegally.

43. Estelle is sweet, but she's _____ about her ideas of what is moral and thinks anyone who disagrees is just plain wrong.

44. Taking small children to eat there is _____ because it's quite a formal restaurant.

45. The candidate's promise to cut taxes was not _____ since she had supported higher taxes for years.

46. Our _____ neighbor deliberately planted a tree right where it would block sunlight for our garden.

47. That book was _____ despite the fact that it didn't sell many copies.

48. Many poems contain _____, which often leads to very different interpretations of their meaning.

49. Ducks and other waterfowl must _____ themselves regularly to remain waterproof.

50. We all wished Jules and Loretta many years of _____ joy as they set off on their honeymoon.

Lesson 29

abound *uh•BOUND* VERB

1. to be plentiful [Trees *abound* in the forest.]

2. to have something in great numbers; to be rich in something [The mall *abounds* with shoppers during the holiday season.]

apathy *AP•uh•thee* NOUN

a lack of interest in something; a lack of caring and involvement [A shrug is a response that shows *apathy*.]

converge *kun•VURJ* VERB

1. to come together at one point [Parallel lines never *converge*.]

2. to move toward each other, toward the same place, or for the same purpose; to meet as a group [Fans started to *converge* in the stadium parking lot long before the game was scheduled to begin.]

dire *DIRE* ADJECTIVE

1. causing horror and suffering; dreadful [The earthquake left the city in a *dire* situation.]

2. urgent or desperate [The accident victims were in *dire* need of medical care.]

dynamic *dy•NAM•ik* ADJECTIVE

active and energetic; having power and force [Melva's *dynamic* approach to the problem got everyone involved in solving it.]

embitter *em•BIT•tur* VERB

to cause to have bitter feelings [Don't let a few people's bad behavior *embitter* you about humanity as a whole.]

humility *hyoo•MIL•ih•tee* NOUN

the quality of being humble, of not being proud or conceited [Accepting the praise with *humility*, the hero insisted that anyone would have done what he did.]

impromptu *im•PROMP•too* ADJECTIVE

without having been thought about beforehand; without preparation [When we all found ourselves at the same restaurant, we had an *impromptu* party.]

malicious *muh•LISH•us* ADJECTIVE

deliberately harmful; showing ill will [They started a *malicious* rumor about Clarence.]

prestige *preh•STEEZH* NOUN

high public regard; reputation or influence based on what is known about one [Megan gained *prestige* by winning the science fair.]

residue *REZ•ih•doo* NOUN

what is left after part is used or removed [The spilled lemonade evaporated but left a *residue* on the counter that I needed to clean up.]

ruse *ROOZ* NOUN

a plan to deceive or mislead; a trick [A bird may pretend to have a broken wing as a *ruse* to draw a dangerous animal away from the nest.]

spurn *SPURN* VERB

to reject with scorn [Don't *spurn* Nate's offer of help; he's only nine, but he has good ideas.]

subdue *sub•DOO* VERB

1. to overcome or conquer [It took days for the army to *subdue* the invaders.]

2. to gain control over; to keep down or hold back [This syrup may *subdue* your cough.]

3. to soften or make less intense; to tone down [A woman spoke to the angry crowd, trying to *subdue* their reaction to the news.]

unconventional *un•kun•VEN•shun•ul* ADJECTIVE not following the usual way of thinking or acting; uncommon [Eating dessert before the main course is *unconventional*.]

During a drive in the country, Max and Min found a frozen lake, got their skates, and had an impromptu practice. After skating around on their own for a bit,

they converged at the center of the lake. Min asked, "Have you seen any ducks?"

Max replied, "No, they've flown south for the winter."

"Oh," Min said in a subdued voice, "then I think the ice is quacking." ■

Words to Go!

Exercise A: True or False
Circle TRUE or FALSE for each statement.

USE A WORD ONLY ONE TIME IN EACH EXERCISE.

1. Roads **abound** with cars during rush hour. . . . . TRUE FALSE
2. **Dynamic** people are often effective leaders. . . . . TRUE FALSE
3. A person shows **humility** by bragging and boasting. . . . . TRUE FALSE
4. Destroying property as an act of vandalism is **malicious**. . . . . TRUE FALSE
5. Getting an unexpected gift from a friend would **embitter** you. . . . . TRUE FALSE
6. A person would **spurn** another person by asking him or her for a date. . . . . . TRUE FALSE
7. England wanted to **subdue** the colonies during the American Revolution. . . . . . . TRUE FALSE

Exercise B: When . . .
Write the Word that best completes each sentence.

8. When people who could vote in an election just don't bother to go to the polls, what they demonstrate is . . . . _____

9. When a musician plays without having memorized a piece and without any sheet music, his or her performance is . . . . _____

10. When the Greeks gave the Trojans a huge, wooden horse in which soldiers were hiding so that they could get inside the walls of Troy to fight, that "gift" was a . . . . _____

11. When the painters known as the Impressionists started painting in a new and different way that many people didn't like or understand, their art at that time was . . . . _____

12. When a college or university is famous for its excellent teaching and the intelligence of its students and the important people who have gone there, it has . . . . _____

Exercise C: Mini-Rhyme Time
Write the Word that best completes each rhyme.

13. Ringing my own doorbell as an excuse to get off the phone is a ___ I use. _____

14. Underpaying the person who looks after the kids may ___ the sitter. _____

15. If the place for stray animals is full, dogs ___ at the pound. _____

16. The stickiness that stays after you peel off a sticker is a ___ of glue. _____

17. To capture and restrain an active female sheep is to ___ a ewe. _____

Exercise D: Antonyms

Write the Word that means the opposite
of each underlined word or phrase.

18. Michael gave a <u>rehearsed</u> speech, but Malcolm just made a few ___ remarks.

_____

19. Since none of the <u>normal and ordinary</u> methods have worked, let's try something ___.

_____

20. Treating people unfairly will ___ them; treating them well will <u>please and gladden</u> them.

_____

21. Some of the people had <u>slight or minor</u> money problems; others lived in ___ poverty.

_____

22. Rather than showing <u>great pride</u> in her accomplishment, Vanessa displayed ___.

_____

23. I wish Lenore wouldn't ___ all of my suggestions; couldn't she <u>accept</u> just one?

_____

24. The senator's brief but inspiring speech turned the crowd's ___ into <u>enthusiasm</u>.

_____

25. If family members <u>scatter</u> to live in different states, it's nice to have a reunion at which they ___.

_____

Exercise E: Synonyms

Write the Word that could be used in place of each underlined word or phrase.

26. The principal was determined to increase the <u>fame and distinction</u> of the school.

_____

27. Fish <u>are numerous</u> in certain parts of the ocean.

_____

28. The librarian tried to <u>quiet down</u> the noisy, active children.

_____

29. Scrape the <u>remainder</u> of food from each plate into the garbage.

_____

30. There are several paths up the hill, but they all <u>join</u> at the top.

_____

31. Our <u>lively, spirited</u> new coach really inspired the team to succeed.

_____

32. Wearing gym shoes with a tuxedo is an <u>unusual</u> combination.

_____

33. After becoming wealthy, Lilah began to <u>cast aside</u> her old friends.

_____

34. Leaving a campfire burning can have <u>terrible</u> consequences.

_____

35. With a <u>hateful</u> grin, she stepped right on the newly planted flowers.

_____

Exercise F: Fill-in

Write the **Word** that best completes each sentence.

36. The table was scattered with crumbs, the only _____ of our huge dinner.

37. The noisy sirens and alarms suggested some _____ emergency had occurred.

38. My grandmother's soups and stews always _____ with both flavor and healthful ingredients.

39. Nothing was set up in advance, but our _____ celebration of the victory turned out to be fun.

40. The two roads that go around the town _____ on the west side to form one highway.

41. I was excited, but Sally showed her _____ about my news by yawning and saying "So what?"

42. On Thanksgiving, we had a rather _____ meal of bologna sandwiches because our stove wasn't working.

43. Vic was afraid that Sandra would _____ his proposal, so he kept his mouth shut.

44. Driving up in a moving van is a _____ used by burglars to keep neighbors from realizing a house is being robbed.

45. Repeated failures can _____ a person and keep him or her from continuing to try.

46. Although he had little _____ during his lifetime, painter Vincent Van Gogh is now much admired.

47. Mr. Ruiz is such a _____ teacher that he can get everyone excited about any subject.

48. One candidate's _____ lies about the other were meant to ruin his reputation.

49. Raymond's _____ kept him from thinking he deserved the prize, and he blushed fiercely when he got it.

50. Trying to _____ the students, Ms. Richmond said, "Please keep your voices down."

Quick LIST

abound V.	**embitter** V.	**residue** N.
apathy N.	**humility** N.	**ruse** N.
converge V.	**impromptu** ADJ.	**spurn** V.
dire ADJ.	**malicious** ADJ.	**subdue** V.
dynamic ADJ.	**prestige** N.	**unconventional** ADJ.

A man called 911 to report that he had been maliciously attacked in the yard in front of his house. A young police officer rushed to the scene to try to capture and subdue the attacker. Fifteen minutes later, she was back. "Case solved," she said.

The chief was impressed. "Wow! That was fast!"

"Aw," said the officer with humility, "it was easy."

"So what happened? And how did you get the black eye?"

"Oh, that," the officer blushed. "I stepped on the same rake the guy did." ■

"But I arrested it, sir!"

Lesson 30

allocate AL•oh•kate VERB

    1. to set aside for a specific purpose [Dana thinks that Congress should *allocate* more money for schools.]

    2. to distribute in shares, even or uneven [Please be sure to *allocate* the available space so that everyone has room for his or her display.]

    Question: What do you call a man who constantly forgets to allocate enough money for clothes and shoes?

Answer: Embarrassed

antagonism an•TAG•uh•niz•um NOUN

    conflict and dislike, such as that between enemies [Merle felt such *antagonism* toward Owen that she couldn't stand to be near him.]

concept KON•sept NOUN

    an idea, especially a general idea [Nikki doesn't understand the *concept* of a partnership; I hope she and I don't have to work together.]

cynical SIN•ih•kul ADJECTIVE

    having a tendency to believe the worst about people [Ed is so *cynical* that he thinks every salesperson is lying to him just to make a sale.]

differentiate dif•ur•EN•shee•ate VERB

    to notice or show a difference [If you can't *differentiate* between the higher-priced product and the cheaper one, buy the cheaper one!]

elite ih•LEET

    NOUN the finest, best, richest, or most powerful part of a group [The restaurant was expensive but popular among the town's *elite*.]

    ADJECTIVE best of its or their kind; looked up to [Harry wanted to join an *elite* fraternity.]

equate ee•KWATE VERB

    to say or suggest that two things are equal [Are you trying to *equate* your little problem with the suffering of homeless people?]

fervent FUR•vunt ADJECTIVE

    showing great warmth or strength of feeling [Part of Myra's goal of becoming a doctor had to do with her *fervent* desire to help people.]

gawky GAW•kee ADJECTIVE

    not graceful in movement; awkward [The *gawky* newborn colt struggled to stand up.]

instill in•STILL VERB

    to put (a feeling or idea) into someone's mind so thoroughly that it strongly influences him or her [Bad experiences with a neighbor's terrier were enough to *instill* in her a dread of all dogs.]

irrational ear•RASH•uh•nul ADJECTIVE

    not using or involving clear thinking; not logical [Fear can lead to *irrational* behavior.]

pliable PLY•uh•bul ADJECTIVE

    1. easily bendable without breaking or cracking [Warm the wax to make it *pliable*.]

    2. easily influenced and controlled by other people [Wanda was a *pliable* child, always willing to go along with her sister's plans.]

speculate SPEK•yoo•late VERB

    1. to think carefully; to consider [We stopped to *speculate* about how to cross the river.]

    2. to guess [I have no idea who will win, and I don't want to *speculate* about it.]

    3. to take a significant risk in the hope of making a profit or gaining an advantage [Some people *speculate* in the stock market; others keep their money in a nice, safe bank.]

stopgap STOP•gap

    NOUN something that is used only until something better or more suitable can be found [Living in a hotel was a *stopgap* until Justin could find an apartment.]

    ADJECTIVE not good enough to be permanent; useful for the time being [We used picnic benches as *stopgap* seats for the dinner table.]

upshot UP•shot NOUN

    the final result [I hit some ice and lost control; the *upshot* was that the car landed in the ditch.]

Exercise A: What It Is

Write the **Word** that each clue describes.

USE A **WORD** ONLY ONE
TIME IN EACH EXERCISE.

1. This kind of dancer probably steps on his or her partner's toes.   _____

2. This is what snobs think of themselves as being.   _____

3. When you make a prediction, you do this about the future.   _____

4. This describes the kind of person who tends to be suspicious.   _____

5. This describes a belief in superstitions.   _____

6. People who are having a feud feel this toward each other.   _____

7. You do this to something when you give out portions of it.   _____

8. Someone who asks "Who won the game?" wants to know this.   _____

9. Examples of this are freedom, truth, and fairness.   _____

10. This describes the kind of fan who goes to every single game.   _____

11. This describes a thing that isn't truly right but is better than nothing.   _____

Exercise B: What It Is Not

Write the **Word** that belongs in each blank.

12. Dotty is stubborn, determined and hard-headed. She never gives up, gives in, or takes suggestions from anyone. Dotty is NOT . . . .   _____

13. Privates in the army are the lowest rank, and they don't get to make a lot of decisions about what they do. They take orders but can't give them. Privates are NOT among the army's . . . .   _____

14. I've bought a number of beat-up, rusty cars so I could get to work. Finally, I saved enough for the car I've always wanted. I'm going to take very good care of it because this one is NOT just a . . . .   _____

15. Keesha always looks on the bright side and assumes that people are basically good. It wouldn't be hard to take advantage of her because she is quite trusting. Keesha is NOT . . . .   _____

16. Rafael sort of enjoys playing baseball, but he likes other things much more. He avoids going to practice, and it doesn't upset him if a game is rained out. Rafael's interest in baseball is NOT . . . .   _____

17. We need to work together cheerfully with cooperation and friendship. We need to support each other and lend a helping hand. We need harmony, NOT . . . .   _____

Exercise C: Analogies

Write the letter of the word pair that completes the analogy.

____ 18. **equate** : **differentiate** ::
  A. lift : carry
  B. look : stare
  C. choose : select
  D. advance : retreat

____ 19. **pliable** : *flexible* ::
  A. fast : rapid
  B. warm : hot
  C. sad : happy
  D. similar : identical

____ 20. **antagonism** : *war* ::
  A. hunger : thirst
  B. labor : exhaustion
  C. doubt : confidence
  D. rudeness : courtesy

Exercise E: Synonyms

Write the Word that could be used in place of each underlined word or phrase.

26. Reciting the Pledge of Allegiance can help to <u>establish</u> feelings of patriotism.

27. If you continue to make <u>unreasonable</u> choices, you'll regret it.

28. I can't <u>distinguish</u> a happy bark from an angry one, so I avoid dogs.

29. Maurice is at that <u>clumsy</u> age where he trips over his own feet.

30. I need to <u>budget</u> an hour of time tonight to write an essay.

31. The <u>outcome</u> of my hard work was that I passed the test.

32. Democracy is based on the <u>thought</u> that everyone has equal value.

33. I decided to <u>gamble</u> on the new company by investing in it.

34. Chip's <u>bitter, gloomy</u> belief is that all politicians are crooks.

35. Pets are not as precious as children, so please don't <u>compare</u> them.

Exercise D: Completion

Choose the correct answer to complete each sentence.

____ 21. Something that most parents try to **instill** in their children is
  A. food.   B. greediness.   C. moral values.

____ 22. An example of something that is **pliable** is
  A. clay.   B. a yo-yo.   C. a baseball bat.

____ 23. **Elite** neighborhoods or clubs are thought of as being
  A. boring.   B. superior.   C. democratic.

____ 24. You have to **differentiate** among things in order to
  A. sort them.   B. store them.   C. collect them.

____ 25. To make a **fervent** request is to
  A. hint.   B. plead.   C. threaten.

A gawky young girl trips and falls down a whole flight of stairs. A man rushes over to help her and asks, "What happened? Did you miss a step?"

"No," the girl answers, "I think I hit them all!" ■

Exercise F: Fill-in

Write the **Word** that best completes each sentence.

36. Giovanni ignored directions, and the _____ was that he got totally confused.

37. I admire Janet and feel no _____ for her even though she's my opponent.

38. Bud couldn't _____ between the two shades of blue; they looked the same to him.

39. It is _____ to think that a foreigner will understand English if it is spoken loudly enough.

40. People who design libraries ought to _____ plenty of room for tables.

41. Many people _____ education and wisdom, but they're really not the same.

42. Sean's parents have a _____ of good parenting that involves a good deal of strictness.

43. Pie-crust dough must be _____, or you can't make it fit into the pan correctly.

44. Stephanie and Sonny belong to that _____ group of students who win all the elections and contests.

45. Many teens become _____ when they grow rapidly, but they eventually learn to walk and run smoothly.

46. The time Dad spent reading aloud helped to _____ in me a lasting love of books.

47. Blair's _____ attitude made her assume that Daria had a selfish reason for helping her.

48. The man gave _____ thanks to the firefighter who had risked death to save him.

49. I'll use a piece of wire as a _____ to hold the license plate on until I can find a bolt.

50. Medical researchers _____ about what might cause certain diseases and then design experiments to test their theories.

Exercise G: Writing

Speculate about your life twenty years from now—your family and home, what you do for fun and for work, and perhaps which classmates you've stayed in touch with. Then, on your own paper, briefly describe your future life, using TWO or more **Words**.

Quick LIST

allocate V.
antagonism N.
concept N.
cynical ADJ.
differentiate V.
elite N., ADJ.
equate V.
fervent ADJ.
gawky ADJ.
instill V.
irrational ADJ.
pliable ADJ.
speculate V.
stopgap N., ADJ.
upshot N.

_____

Question:
What happened to the guy who couldn't differentiate between his toothpaste and his window putty?

Answer: The upshot was that his window panes fell out, but his gums and teeth are stronger than ever.

"I speculate that I won't have to brush again for another twenty years!"

Word Fun 6!

Digging

Find and underline the **Word** from Unit 6 that is buried in each sentence.
The words to dig up are *allot, apathy, dally, dauntless, dire,* and *ornery.*

1. Sit in the corner, you stubborn, bad-tempered child, you!

2. Get out of bed. All your lazing around is going to make you late!

3. If there's a flood, I really think we will be in urgent need of immediate help.

4. If the helping you take is small, others will be able to receive their fair share.

5. On your travels through life, if you don't care enough to choose a path, your route will always be downhill.

6. No one was more daring than my determined aunt. Lesser women would have given up long ago.

Boxing

Fill in each set of blanks with a word you know that matches the clue.
The boxed letters will spell out the answer to the question on the right.

Burp!

1. An animal infamous for its odor . . . .

2. One member of a marital relationship . . . .

3. The residue of a fire . . . .

4. What can be pungent, besides a taste . . . . . .

5. Another word for *elation* . . . .

6. Another word for *breadth* . . . .

Question: What do you call a **bird** that has been eaten by a cat?

Answer: a

Rhyming

Make each poem rhyme and have a poetic rhythm by
substituting a **Word** from Unit 6 for the underlined words.

1. Oh, yes, the way she looks is quite intentional.
   She likes to be completely <u>not in line with accepted standards</u>.

   _____

2. I hope you don't expect me to excuse
   Your use of such a sneaky, tricky <u>sneaky trick</u>.

   _____

3. We have three beagles and a basset hound,
   Four cats, two birds . . . at our house, pets <u>exist in large numbers</u>.

   _____

Puzzling

Identify the **Word** from Unit 6 that fits the clue in each box.

1. c _____

2. i _____

TOP

3. a _____

"I DO" RINGS
GROOM BRIDE
"I PR___NCE
YO___KE
RELA____HIP
HONEYMOON
HOUSE FAMILY

4. m _____

5. e _____

Planning

Two friends were discussing their marital goals. The first, a placid young woman, said the only thing that mattered was that her husband love her completely.

The second woman's concept of marriage was more dynamic, and other things *did* matter. So she planned to get married four times. Her husbands would be a banker, an actor, a hair stylist, and an undertaker.

When her friend asked why, she replied, "Isn't that obvious? It's one for the money,

Naming

Match each description to the name it goes best with.

____ 1. She feels your pain; she feels your joy.

____ 2. He's in charge of budgeting the funds.

____ 3. What a lively, energetic person she is!

____ 4. You won't catch this guy bragging.

____ 5. She's always ready to pick a fight.

____ 6. This guy is just plain immense!

A. Al O'Kayt

B. Vi Karriyus

C. Stu Pendus

D. Di Nammik

E. Hugh Millitee

F. Ann Taganizim

two for the show,

three to get ready,

and four to go!"

"On the other hand, . . ."

Word Fun Answers!

Unit 1, pages 38–39

DEFINING
1. C   4. B
2. D   5. A
3. E   6. F

DIGGING
1. infer; in fertile
2. sedate; used a term
3. renown; are now noticed

RHYMING
1. manifest
2. abashed
3. recoil
4. appease

CROSSING
Across
1. empathy
4. bias
7. amass
9. dawdle
10. irk
12. astute
13. induce
14. retort
Down
2. measly
3. testy
4. bleak
5. squander
6. tirade
8. vigil
11. lush
12. apt

Unit 2, pages 60–61

BOXING
1. fad
2. brush
3. teach
4. loan
5. brakes
6. blame
7. gray
Answer: frankly

MATCHING
1. G
2. D   5. B
3. E   6. C
4. F   7. A

NAMING
1. F   5. A
2. E   6. D
3. B   7. H
4. C   8. G

RHYMING
1. curt
2. unwary

SEARCHING
Suggested answers
1. top
2. back
3. gasp
4. turn
5. sins
6. cranky
7. mess
8. flood

Unit 3, pages 82–83

CROSSING
Across
2. admonish
6. attire
7. grim
8. canny
9. docile
12. ostracize
Down
1. snare
2. avarice
3. haggard
4. align
5. roundabout
10. legacy
11. wince

DIGGING
1. stoic; seems to. I can't
2. botch; robot. Change
3. wan; saw a new
4. oaf; to a fool
5. daft; did afterwards
6. distort; said is torture

DEFINING
1. E
2. D   4. B
3. A   5. C

PUZZLING
1. chronological
2. excruciating
3. jargon
4. congenial

MATCHING
1. E
2. D   4. C
3. B   5. A

Unit 4, pages 104–105

BOXING
1. <u>S</u>unday
2. no<u>i</u>se
3. tes<u>t</u>
4. <u>y</u>ell<u>o</u>w
5. h<u>u</u>rry
6. <u>s</u>orry
7. <u>e</u>nd
8. <u>l</u>ock
9. <u>f</u>irst
Answer: "Suit yourself."

NAMING
1. B
2. E
3. D
4. A
5. I
6. F
7. H
8. J
9. G
10. C

A-MAZE-ING
1 *Right* erratic
2 *Down* coexist
3 *Left* transient
4 *Up* tepid
5 *Right* depict
6 *Down* tyranny

DEFINING
1. D
2. E
3. C
4. B
5. A

Unit 5, pages 126–127

NAMING
1. F
2. D
3. A
4. B
5. E
6. C

DEFINING
1. E
2. C
3. F
4. D
5. B
6. A

PUZZLING
1. deteriorate *or* decrepit
2. heart-rending
3. egotist
4. fluctuate

DIGGING
1. laud; ful<u>l auditorium</u>
2. reverie; fo<u>rever, I</u> entertained
3. assent; cla<u>ss enth</u>usiastically
4. candid; toni<u>c, and I d</u>ished

SEARCHING
Suggested answers
1. sad
2. dim
3. fox
4. hard
5. war
6. even
7. fat

RHYMING
1. dexterity
2. rebuff
3. rubble
4. suffice

Unit 6, pages 148–149

DIGGING
1. ornery; <u>c</u>orner, <u>y</u>ou
2. dally; be<u>d. All y</u>our
3. dire; floo<u>d, I really</u>
4. allot; sm<u>all, others</u>
5. apathy; <u>a path, y</u>our
6. dauntless; determine<u>d aunt. Less</u>er

BOXING
1. <u>s</u>kunk
2. <u>w</u>ife
3. <u>a</u>sh
4. sme<u>ll</u>
5. <u>j</u>oy
6. <u>w</u>idth
Answer: a swallow

RHYMING
1. unconventional
2. ruse
3. abound

PUZZLING
1. converge
2. instill
3. acme
4. marital
5. elapse

NAMING
1. B
2. A
3. D
4. E
5. F
6. C

MADGE: Oooo! that word *cowardice* just makes me cringe. But I do like *cowtail*.

ISABEL: Dearie, put your reading glasses on.

Question: Where do infamous people fill their gas tanks?
Answer: At the villain station

Question: What do you call a robot that never takes the optimum route?
Answer: R2Detour

Word Index

Question: How did the uncouth garbage collector break up with his girl friend?

Answer: He dumped her—literally!

Well, we made it! *(Thank goodness!)* You did very good work, and I'm so proud of you. Wait! Josette, should you be reading this page? I don't think you've turned in all your writing exercises. . . . Oh, a week ago? . . . Okay, then I'm sure it's right here, um, near the top.

In the meantime, I'd love to hear from any of you who want to write and tell me

- what you enjoyed about Words to Go!
- what you didn't enjoy.
- whether you found any mistakes.
- which was your favorite joke or picture.
- which kind of exercise you enjoyed most.
- what you think is the best word of all the 450 words.
- what you speculated, in Lesson 30, your life would be like twenty years from now.

Don't tell me *all* of those things! I already have lots of paperwork to finish before summer. And then, you know, I have to plan my wedding. And finish building the house. And practice for the Olympic tryouts. And, gosh, is astronaut training before or after the wedding? And did I schedule obedience classes for the dogs? And! Where! Are! Josette's! Writing! Exercises!

(Deep breath, Molly. Deep breath. You're not as neat and well-organized as you used to be, but you're still good at . . . breathing deeply.)

Well, I'll make time to read your letters. Please tell me your name, your grade, and your school's name. Mail letters to me at this address:

Miss Morgenstern
Perfection Learning
10520 New York Avenue
Des Moines, Iowa 50322-3775